WE ARE
MADE IN BRUNEL®

LONDON
DESIGN
FESTIVAL

Made in Brunel is proud to be a part of
the London Design Festival 2020.

WE ARE
MADE IN BRUNEL®

Foreword

2020 has been a very different year. The COVID-19 pandemic and the lockdown it caused in March meant that, for the first time in the history of Brunel Design, the final year students were not able to complete their major project prototypes in the departmental workshops and, as a first since Made in Brunel was launched in 2006, the exhibition could not be held in the physical world.

It was under these circumstances that our strong culture of collaboration made all the difference. Following the campus closure and a swift response to the lockdown regulations by the department, the students managed to finalise the major projects collaborating with the academic supervisors online and submitting the work as high-quality digital models, while the very efficient Made in Brunel team ensured this book is produced working from home and the showcase takes place across several digital channels. The book – symbolically titled 'We are Made in Brunel' – presents the best of these collaborative efforts in the challenging times.

Although very demanding, the academic year 2019/2020 has not been all doom and gloom. The year has also been marked by two highly positive events, which are bound to redefine the design education at Brunel in the years to come. The first event is the formal establishment of Brunel Design School, which will unite the Department of Design and the Division of Digital Media from the Department of Electronic and Computer Engineering with a view of growing the educational provision in digital design, in particular in the areas such as digital product and service design. Secondly, Brunel has gained membership in Design Factory Global Network, an alliance of 31 innovation centres at leading universities and research organisations spanning five continents of the world. This membership will enable a number of international cooperation activities, adding to the student experience in the new School.

In hope that life goes back to normal soon, I wish all graduates of 2019/2020 a very successful future.

Dr Vanja Garaj
Head of Design

CONTE

NTS

We Are...

Every year, Made in Brunel strives to represent Brunel Design in the most inclusive way to promote and showcase all student work to the wider community. This year we became 'We Are Made in Brunel', bringing the focus back to us, the students that empower it. As a student-led initiative, this allows us to have autonomy over how we promote the designers of Brunel 2020.

As the year comes to a close we have the opportunity to reflect on the achievements of the year, all the fantastic events held, and work produced. We kicked off the year with the annual Brand Launch, an event designed to get all those in the Brunel Design Community together, celebrating the new brand. In January, we set about producing a very successful Pop-Up event on Shoreditch High Street, attended by over 200 industry professionals and students. Final year work-in-progress was reviewed, and talks from Brunel Design alumni were hosted offering an insight into their journeys and experiences in the design industry.

Next came the annual Industrial Review Evenings, specifically designed to get feedback on major projects, and offering funding opportunities. The work shown did us proud, and a fantastic couple of evenings were had, paving the way for some of our student's work to gain industry recognition and backing. The 24 Hour design challenge was another highlight of the year offering a fun and testing event for students in all years with industry briefs to complete for student portfolio projects.

The culmination of every year, an event that every design student aspires to is the Brunel design showcase at the OXO Tower on the banks of the Thames. Sadly, like most events this summer, it had to be cancelled due to the COVID-19 pandemic. However, determined to still showcase our work, the production of this book became the big focus. Increased social media coverage and the launch of the 'Isolation Work Station' also helped to engage the Brunel design community.

Here we are, at the end of all the hard work. The We Are Made in Brunel book along with the 2020 digital portfolio. We could not be prouder of the team, their passion, kindness and humility throughout the year has been a breath of fresh air during an otherwise tough time.

We hope you enjoy reading this publication – a collection of diverse inventive design solutions and we wish every Brunel Design student the very best in their future endeavours.

We are Made in Brunel.

Amber Sayers & Jack Day
Directors
Made in Brunel 2020

Events

This year we have had the pleasure of taking on the roles of event managers as part of the Made in Brunel team and are proud of what we have been able to achieve. In November, we revealed the 'We Are Made in Brunel' brand to the design community, at our launch event. Throughout the evening we unveiled our six core principles and showcased the process behind this years' brand. Following on from the launch, we hosted the annual sketch off and 24 hour design challenge, where students had the opportunity to work on briefs set by companies such as Cambridge Consultants, Lego and Shark Ninja. During the 24 hour design challenge students were tasked with researching, ideating, developing and presenting their final concepts under time pressure. These events gave students an opportunity to apply their knowledge to a range of briefs as well as demonstrate to potential employers the diversity within their skill set.

January saw our biggest event of the year, the Made in Brunel Pop Up. This event was the perfect opportunity for final year and masters students to showcase their work in progress. The sell-out event consisted of talks from Brunel alumni followed by drinks, canapes and an evening of networking. Our industry review evenings in February gave students the chance to discuss the direction of their project with industry specialists and their peers. This provided invaluable insights enabling students to move forward with their projects. Unfortunately, due to the current pandemic we were unable to host our end of year showcase at the Oxo Tower where students would have presented their projects to design professionals, alumni and the general public. However, the whole team has worked hard to find alternative ways to showcase our year's work and connect students with industry. We would like to thank everyone who attended and supported our events throughout the year, we hope that you enjoyed them as much as we did.

Oliver Martin & Caitlin Beer
Events Managers
Made in Brunel 2020

Brunel Design School

The Department of Design (Brunel Design) have joined forces with the Division of Digital Media (Brunel Digital), previously within the Department of Electronic and Computer Engineering, to form Brunel Design School.

Becoming operational as of September, 2020, the School will provide a platform to expand the scope of the design education at Brunel from the traditional industrial and product design aimed at the manufacturing sector into a range of digital design areas, including digital product and service design, user experience (UX) design, motion graphics and visual effects. The School curriculum will be organised along two interconnected pathways: physical and digital. The new digital pathway will adopt our long-standing educational approach of linking design and engineering in fostering both creativity and making skills - with the digital pathway focusing on coding as an analogy to the physical workshop-based prototyping in the physical pathway.

With nearly 1000 students and 100 staff across 12 undergraduate, postgraduate-taught and postgraduate-research programmes, Brunel Design School will aim to position itself as a leader in the digital design education, thus responding to the creative talent demand by the growing digital economy in the UK and worldwide. While expanding the digital provision, the School will continue nurturing its traditionally leading product and industrial design programmes and seek the opportunities to create the curricular synergies between the physical and digital domains.

Brunel and COVID-19

Brunel Design is known for making things. The name of our brand 'Made in Brunel' speaks for itself.

Our workshop facilities, technicians and highly creative students all go together to make practical work of an outstanding quality every year.

So, it was with disbelief and enormous disappointment that we had to shut the doors of our workshops when the country went into lockdown on 23rd March. For the past 40 years our final year students have produced prototypes and models as part of their final year major projects. 2020 is the first year that major projects are largely digitally rendered. Fortunately, the students had all submitted their contextual design models a few days before lockdown and it is interesting to compare in this book the photographed physical models of contextual to the mainly rendered images of the major projects. I hope that next year we will see a return of students to workshops, bringing with it that invaluable experience of making and testing that is such an important part of what we do at Brunel.

I assumed that when the university went into lockdown at the time that it would be the last I would see of the workshops for many weeks. However, two days later an enquiry came into the university to see if we could assist with some 3D printing for the Royal Brompton and Harefield NHS Trust. The clinical engineering team there were researching into converting existing items of equipment such as domiciliary ventilators into ventilators to treat COVID-19 patients in critical care. The idea was brilliantly simple; using 3D printed adaptors of various designs, each machine could be connected to the hospital oxygen supply and the oxygen then pumped via a mask to the patient. Many journeys back and forth from the 3D printing lab at Brunel to the hospital followed over the next few weeks and we managed to convert many machines, giving the hospital some much needed extra capacity at the height of the crisis.

The research into the use of 3D printing to help fight COVID-19 is continuing and it is hoped that this work will benefit countries worldwide in the future.

Around the same time, there was a global shortage of PPE to protect frontline staff. One of these items was the protective face visor. Almost immediately, a British war time spirit kicked in with individuals and organisations putting both their staff and facilities to good use to help manufacture extra PPE to help the cause.

Our close links with St Thomas's NHS trust gave us our first opportunity to help with this. They had set up a facility in partnership with the 3D printer manufacturer iMakr to 3D print and manufacture thousands of visors to supply the London hospitals. Many of our students and alumni volunteered to work unpaid at the facility; many travelling great distances every day to work long hours there.

We were keen to put our own 3D printers to good use to help local hospitals and care homes, some of which had been unable to source any PPE at all. Things started on a small scale when I set up a few small printers at home but it wasn't long before many students, staff and alumni came forward with offers of help and we soon went from producing a few visors a day to a few hundred a week. Our team steadily grew; with people 3D printing from home, making visors in the workshops and taking orders through our social media channels. At its height, we had 17 volunteers and 25 3D printers manufacturing 800 visors a week, with daily deliveries across West London. It was a challenge to keep up with demand, with rising infections and deaths, we concentrated our efforts on care homes, many of which were in desperate need of help, and with rising infection rates and deaths in care homes, we concentrated our efforts into helping them in particular.

By the start of June, when we started to wind things down, we had produced a total of 5000 visors and supplied around 80 different organisations. Our main goal from the start was to try to help protect the people who were the real heroes during this crisis. We only had to make a delivery of visors to a care home or hospital and be met with gratitude, smiles and sometimes even tears of relief to give us the motivation to carry on.

Looking back, we are extremely proud to have been able to put our skills and workshops to good use during this troubling time. Every year, Made in Brunel is a fine example of teamwork at its very best, and for very different reasons 2020 was no exception. We could not have done any of it without the dedication of all the staff and students who got involved. Unfortunately, there were far too many people involved to thank individually here, but a huge thank you goes out to you all!

A special thank you must go to the Brunel Design's *sharper alumni for donating money to help with the cause and to Warner Media for sponsoring our visor making. Without their generosity none of this would have been possible.

Paul Josse
Technical Manager, Design & Manufacture

BLACK LIVES MATTER

We have been reading, listening and educating ourselves on the discrimination that BAME people face on a daily basis. No matter what race or colour, we all need to stand together and unite to fight racism. We pledge to continue to learn, grow and do better.

Made in Brunel has been collaborating with students this year, giving them an opportunity to speak out and use our platform to express their views on racial prejudice within the design community.

"Racism has continuously plagued our reality. It has taken its toll on our psyche, our mental health, and our bodies over time. Although it has been far too long a journey, I believe that if we can come together and create an open dialogue where we can all have input, we can change the narrative and build a better and truly inclusive community for everyone in it."

- Tanaka Kungwengwe

"There needs to be more representation and the Brunel design department needs to acknowledge that there is more to design history than what we were taught in our first year. There needs to be a shift in teaching which will encourage not only more POC taking the courses but encourage more POC to look into design as a viable career path.

It has been hard for me as a black person to feel worthy and good enough as a designer when all I've been shown is that the most recognised and influential designers are all white, and that simply is not the case."

- Jayda Bailey

"We all need to do more to fight racism. It is not enough to simply not be racist, but we must be anti-racist. Made in Brunel and Brunel Design Society have come together to write a letter to the Brunel Design Department and encourage them to take proactive action again racism in design. We want to ensure all BAME students are given positive experiences and role models as designers, and feel represented as designers and as people.

We all need to come together, regardless of race, to educate and learn, and send the message that the systematic oppression of black and ethnic minority people is not okay. I hope that the letter inspires positive change within the design department and ensures all designers feel represented at Brunel."

- Hannah Coombs

"We see you. We hear you. We support you. We stand with you." **#blacklivesmatter**

Degree Journey

Most of the projects shown in this book come from the final stages of the undergraduate programmes at Brunel. However, they are only made possible by the preceding two years (and optional year in industry/international exchange), which give Brunel designers their strong base of knowledge and skill, and help them develop into the diverse group of design thinkers whose ideas fill the following pages.

Industrial Design and Technology BA (IDT)
Product Design Engineering BSc (PDE)
Product Design BSc (PD)

Professional Practice

(Optional)

1st Year

Core Modules

Design Process 1

Graphic Communication

Workshop Tutorials

2nd Year

Design Process 2

Design Communication

Design for Manufacture

Course-Specific Modules

IDT

Creative Engineering Practice

Product Analysis

PD & PDE

Electronics and Mathematics

Mechanics for Design

IDT

Systems Design

Design Applications

PD & PDE

Dynamics, Mechanisms & Stress Analysis

Electronics, Programming & Interfacing

PhD

See more on pg. 214

3rd Year

Core Modules

Major Project

Design & Innovation,
Management and Process

Course-Specific Modules

IDT

Contextual Design

PD

Human Factors

PDE

Computer Based Design Methods

Optional Modules

Graphic Communication 3

Environmentally Sensitive Design

Contextual Design

Human Factors

Computer Based Design Methods

Masters

Integrated Product Design MSc

**Sustainability, Entrepreneurship
and Design MSc**

See more on pg. 186

Design, Strategy and Innovation MA

Design and Branding Strategy MA

See more on pg. 206

Placements & Exchanges

The placement year is a key part of the design courses at Brunel. Throughout the years we have developed strong links with industry, allowing us to gain real life experience and explore within the design field, with placements lasting 3, 6, 9 or 12 months. In addition, Brunel also offers the opportunity for students to take part in a university exchange scheme with educational establishments worldwide. Alternatively, students have the option to use this year to focus on personal ventures and startups, getting an early foothold in industry.

82
in the UK

Dyson, Jaguar Land Rover, Mondelez International, Cambridge Consultants, Williams F1, Bosch...

13
International placements

In Germany, Denmark, Portugal, China, Malaysia, Hong Kong, India and the Netherlands

7
International exchanges

Politechnico di Milano, TU Delft, San Francisco State University and Institut Supérieur de Design

87%
of students secured placements in London

IBM, SharkNinja, Guy's and St Thomas'
NHS Foundation Trust, Therefore, Disney,
Haberdashery, BatchWorks, BIOHM...

4
Startup businesses

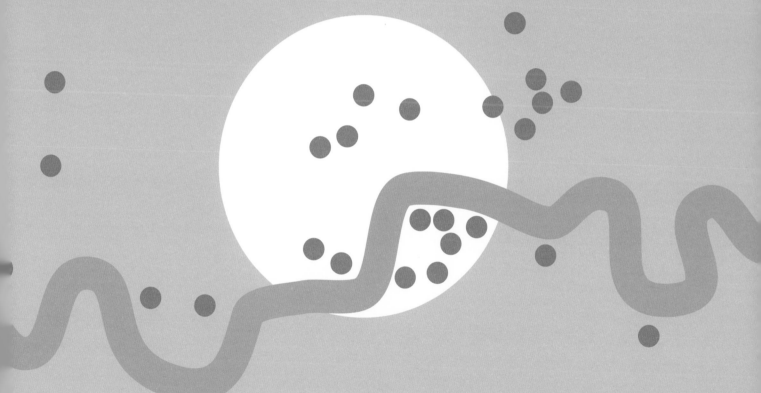

These opportunities are provided with
support and guidance from the Brunel
Professional Development Centre.
To find out more or get in contact,
visit **brunel.ac.uk/pdc.**

DESIGN AND INNOVATION, MANAGEMENT AND PROCESS

Dr Richard Evans
Senior Lecturer in Human Factors, Module Leader

Launching a new product or service into a new market is a high-risk strategy. Scholars estimate that 60-90% of start-up companies fail to satisfy the anticipated requirements of potential customers. Innovation in design is one of the strongest driving forces for successfully launching new products. The Design & Innovation, Process & Management (DIMP) module explores relevant entrepreneurial principles, theories and methods for organising and managing significant design and innovation activity. Delivered over two terms, it seeks to develop students' strategic planning skills and encourage entrepreneurial thinking. By examining how start-up companies are created and how risks of failure are minimised, students develop independent research skills and their ability for critical thinking. The module aims to develop the student's capacity to apply knowledge, tools and techniques to the creation of unique business models for their designs; they identify appropriate marketing strategies and communication channels to deliver strategic plans effectively.

HUMAN FACTORS

Dr Gabriella Spinelli
Reader in Design Innovation, Module Leader

It is undoubted that design interventions are more successful if the end users are placed at the centre of the design process. To do so, in this module we explore and learn how the design of artefacts, including products, services and systems, can be improved by considering people's cognitive and physical characteristics and their social and emotional aspirations as design requirements. This fundamentally means placing people at the centre of the design process and making sure that design solutions are iteratively evaluated in collaboration with the end users. To understand the characteristics as well as the limitations that humans are endowed with, the module covers topics related to the physiology of the human body as well as cognitive processing and causes and type of human error. The module is centred on design and evaluation methods that aid the development of design interventions that are intuitive, provide users with confidence and improve the overall experience.

ENVIRONMENTALLY SENSITIVE DESIGN

Professor David Harrison
Professor of Design Research, Module Leader

The terrible events of this pandemic year have given many people more time to reflect on the natural world and our relationship with nature. The Environmentally Sensitive Design course at Brunel aims to develop an understanding of environmental problems, and guide students to integrate design strategies, approaches and tools to design low environmental impact products. Approaches explored include eco design, design for behaviour change, emotionally durable design and biomimetics. Students are encouraged to adopt a broader perspective on design for sustainability, not only focused on products but also on innovation in services and business models. The goal is for them to be able to integrate these elements into a personal position on environmental matters, so that environmental issues will play an integral part in their professional design careers.

COMPUTER BASED DESIGN METHODS

Dr Timothy Minton
Lecturer in Computer Aided Design,, Materials and Manufacture, Module Leader

Computer Based Design Methods is a series of integrated projects exploring multiple software packages for CAD visualisation, simulation and reverse engineering. Starting with a blueprint a model car is created using surface modelling techniques. The scale models are 3D printed in high resolution and the digital design is tested using a virtual human testing environment. A lifting jack is prepared and analysed whilst raising the car previously modelled. The car jack parts are tested using finite element analysis (FEA) and motion studies within SolidWorks, combined with optimisation studies to reduce the material requirement whilst maintaining a suitable factor of safety. The second project introduces 3D scanning to reverse engineer an object and thermo-fluid simulation via computational fluid dynamics The module is popular with both staff and students and affords a fantastic opportunity to showcase CAD/CAM/CAE skills with multiple industry standard software packages as well as learning new skills in virtual prototyping, modelling and simulation.

MAJOI
PROJE

Dr Busayawan Lam
Senior Lecturer in Design Innovation

The Major Project module was designed to encourage problem-based learning and integrative studies. Students are expected to work on a self-chosen or industry-based project, which will challenge them to explore new knowledge, as well as apply all knowledge and skills that they have learned and mastered in previous years, such as design for manufacturing, communication design and research. Up to now, Brunel Design students have supported various organisations (large and small; for-profit and not-for-profit; product-based and service-based) in solving their design problems. Through this module, students are able to demonstrate their ability to plan and manage an independent project and come up with original design solutions. The outcomes of this module have led to many innovative products/services in the marketplace and a number of successful design entrepreneurs.

Mia Alamo
Industrial Design and Technology BA

Mina

Mina creates a platform for young individuals with Dyslexia to connect and share problems, information and products. Mina becomes an essential companion for those with Dyslexia.

Dyslexia is a learning disability which has various symptoms including difficulty with reading and comprehension and causes issues with working memory transfer. 16% of the UK population have Dyslexia with it ranging in different degrees of severity.

The gap identified is in the lack of recognition and support for young adults coping with Dyslexia and the negativity surrounding the stigma of the label. The majority of the existing market for dyslexia friendly products are extreme in terms of functionality and price, and typically are created with a younger generation in mind, this leaves a gap for a product which is both affordable and functional for adolescents. Mina is a platform that works to alleviate symptoms and effects caused by Dyslexia and is age appropriate for 18-23 years.

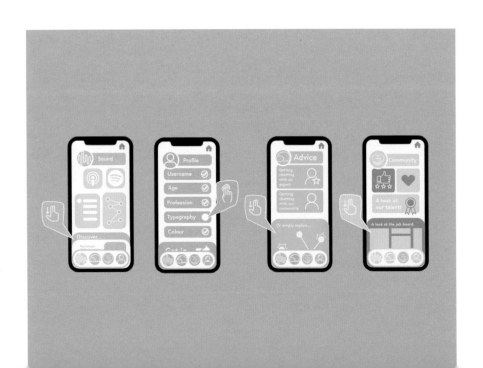

Toby Allen
Industrial Design and Technology BA

Micro Sampler

Micro Sampler is a microplastics sampling device that can be used by secondary schools to educate children on the problems our oceans are facing.

750 tons of plastic is thought to be dumped in our oceans daily. Plastics break up into 'microplastics' which are able to find their way into our food system via aquatic and bird life. A single litre of seawater can contain 8.3 million particles of microplastics.

This portable device has the ability to extract microplastics from sediment samples via density separation. A 30 page activity book takes students through two days of environmentally sensitive activities. Students are guided through the sampling processes before completing a redesign task using the knowledge gained from their activities. The book encourages students by offering prizes to those who display extraordinary creativity, problem solving or critical thinking. The Micro Sampler product aims to build relationships between children and their environment, thus developing an environmental consciousness in later life.

Awarded Ede & Ravencroft Prize 2020

Charlotte Bassett
Product Design Engineering BSc

ToSew

ToSew aims to re-spark the joys surrounding sewing, aimed at young adults aged 18-30. It provides a fresh outlook on sewing, from an outdated task to a social and fun pastime.

ToSew is an app which works alongside a simplified sewing machine, with the aim of encouraging upcycling and sustainable clothing behaviours. The ToSew machine helps reduce the learning time required to start mastering this skill. This is achieved by offering only one stitch type, a clear threading path and a larger working space to allow for ease of use. An accelerometer on the machine's needle records the user's time spent sewing by detecting when the needle is moving. This information is relayed back to the user through the app. Competitions between friends and the community can take place, and trophies can be won.

The app acts as a social media-based platform allowing the community to share designs and help each other directly. The app also provides education surrounding clothing sustainability; helping with buying, washing, upcycling and disposing of clothing.

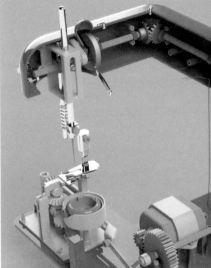

Caitlin Beer
Industrial Design and Technology BA

Memory Pod

Memory Pod aims to support a more fulfilling life for those living with dementia, using a combination of reminiscence therapy and effective communication.

Memory Pod aims to encourage conversation between individuals with dementia and their loved ones/carers. Rather than focusing on improving deteriorating skills which can be frustrating and counterproductive, Memory Pod encourages those emotionally laden recollection skills that are generally more accessible for a person with dementia. Photographs of special moments in a person's life are slotted into the device and trigger music or voice messages which enhance memories associated with the photo.

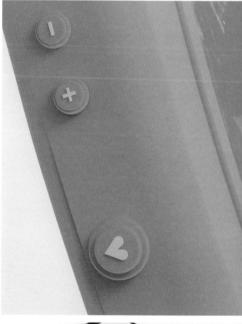

The device aims to support memories shared between loved ones as well as reflecting on those experienced in the past. The accompanying app enables users to share moments from all over the world. Additionally, an educational booklet is provided, describing the difficulties that a person with dementia may be facing and guiding the reader through simple tips to support effective communication.

Helen Bellhouse
Industrial Design and Technology BA

HEAR

HEAR is a learning aid that enables hearing impaired students to attend mainstream lessons, closing the grade-gap for deaf students.

HEAR for deaf children is a project that aims to give back the freedom to learn to hearing impaired students. Hearing impaired students are increasingly put into mainstream schools where there are no specialist provisions. The National Deaf Children's society found that the average grade for deaf children is a D grade. For children with no disability, it is a strong C.

HEAR aims to close the grade gap for children with a hearing impairment without the cost of additional specialist staff. The biggest pain-point for hearing impaired students is the natural decline in academic performance due to difficulty when understanding all the information presented to them. This device will be an assisted learning aid that will help the child actively take part in lessons and revisit anything they have misunderstood in their own time.

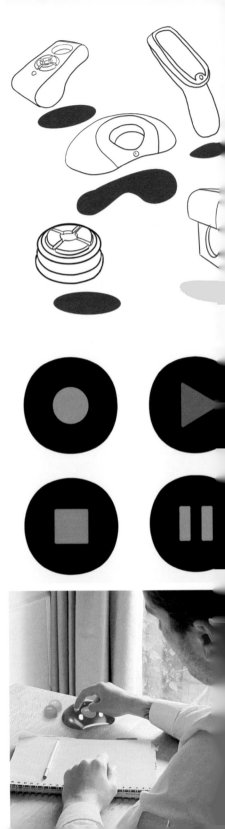

Yash Bhansali
Product Design BSc

Flight Friendly Food

Airplane food - some choose to eat, some choose not to eat, and the rest choose to eat elsewhere. This proposal highlights what could be the next evolution of in-flight meals.

In the last two decades, flight catering systems have made steady improvements to the quality of airline meals. However, economy class passengers continue to hold unfavourable perceptions of food quality, packaging and report a dissatisfying experience overall. This results in a high volume of un-consumed food, amounting to 1.1bn tons of annual waste and $3bn in economic losses.

This solution challenges the current model, addressing passengers' needs through improved packaging functionality and convenience. Food can be pre-booked and collected at the airport prior to boarding from the retailer, Pret A Manger, which strives to close the loop. The proposal provides a glimpse into a future where we may have to balance our expectations as consumers with sustainability and exercise our own choice to enjoy in-flight meals.

Charlie Boyle
Product Design Engineering BSc

Phloss

An inclusively designed and sustainability-focused flossing alternative that uses a service system to distribute refills and utilise waste material, supporting a circular economy.

Interproximal cleaning - the removal of plaque from between teeth - is essential in reducing the risk of gum disease which can influence health throughout the body. Flossing is the most common means of interproximal cleaning but all current methods have a range of associated problems including user motivation, physical accessibility and waste production.

Phloss is a refillable flossing aid that maintains tension in the floss by simply twisting its base. The arms give users with reduced dexterity the ability effortlessly to reach all of their teeth and speed up the cleaning process. To manage the waste, a system has been designed using compostable floss refills. These refills are delivered to people using a subscription service and the used floss refills can be sent back to the manufacturer for industrial composting, utilising waste material and following a circular economy.

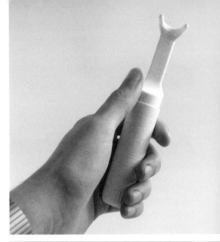

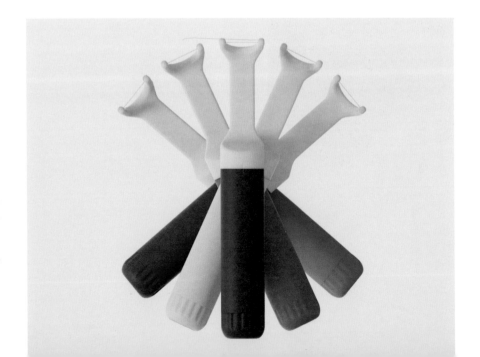

Tom Brew
Industrial Design and Technology BA

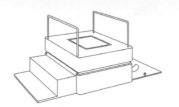

AntiFall Fitness

This stool addresses the barriers stopping seniors from exercising, to allow them to safely use appropriate exercise and thereby reduce their risk of falling.

As a person ages muscle weakness causes impaired gait and balance issues which massively increases the risk of a fall. This risk of falling can be greatly reduced by appropriate exercise, however there are many barriers stopping the elderly from exercising; lack of knowledge, fear of injury and being self-conscious are some examples of the barriers.

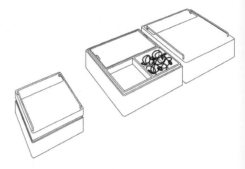

The AntiFall Fitness Stool provides a safe, convenient and simple method of doing appropriate exercise for reducing the risk of a fall. The stool folds out into an exercise station designed specifically for seniors wanting to reduce their risk of falling and improve their quality of life. It allows users to exercise in the safety of their own home and the built-in screen provides guidance on how to correctly perform the exercises to prevent injuries.

Arthur Brooks
Industrial Design and Technology BA

FurPlus

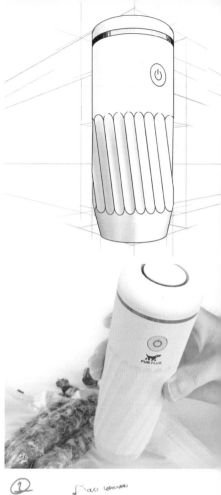

FurPlus is a service aimed at turning domestic food waste into balanced, nutritious food for pet dogs.

With the FurPlus app you now have the power to reduce your food waste while also making healthy, nutritious food for not only your pet but thousands of others, all from your pocket. With the ability to tailor the food you receive to each specific dog thanks to the pet log on the supporting app, you can rest easy knowing that they are getting the perfect balance of nutrients in healthy, appropriate portions.

In support of the app, FurPlus also offers a handheld vacuum sealer that helps turn an already efficient cycle into a near seamless and stress-free experience. With a cyclical design at its core, FurPlus boasts minimal waste, with both the food and the collection bags being reused. This leads to a happy planet, a happy user and a happy dog.

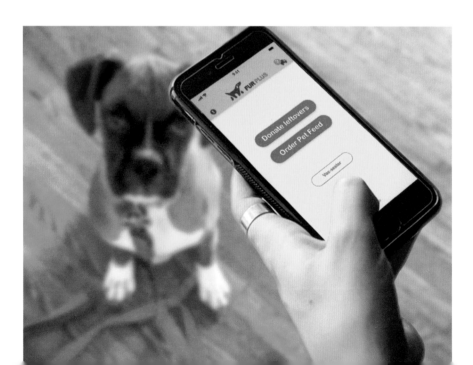

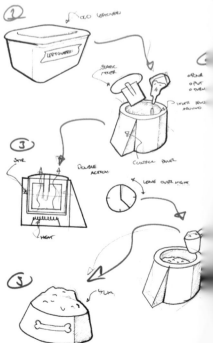

Jake Brown
Product Design Engineering BSc

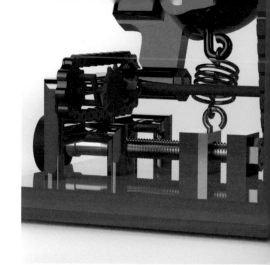

Grip Assist

A fun and engaging way to train grip strength to promote continued and consistent development for better long-term results.

Grip strength is an essential part of everyday life. It deteriorates at an increasing rate as we grow older, with the trait found to be a key concern for seniors during research, but regular hand and wrist movement has been shown to prevent and even reverse this. Furthermore, grip training is an important process for recovering stroke patients and has been shown to help relieve pain for those struggling with lateral epicondylalgia.

Unlike other products on the market, Grip assist focuses on incorporating regular hand and wrist movement into a fun and simple game to encourage frequent and regular use with adjustable resistance to suit all users. The user grips the lever to release game pieces and rotates the handle to control a collection pot to catch as many as they can, scoring points in doing so.

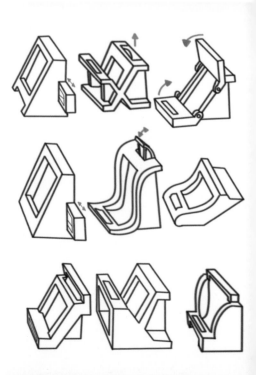

Emily Browne
Product Design Engineering BSc

Fika

An inclusive dining set for all the family; designed to tackle exclusion for children with Cerebral Palsy in their family meal times.

During family mealtimes, children with Cerebral Palsy may have to use different furniture or sit separately from family, leading to feelings of anxiety and exclusion. Physical and eating difficulties often result in a need to use wheelchairs with supportive features that optimise positioning. Everyday dining furniture doesn't have the required functionality to include these children without adaptations. In contrast, assistive furniture designed for disability feels clinical in modern dining environments.

Fika is a family of chairs, with one adapted to the postural and support needs of children with Cerebral Palsy by including fully adjustable arm rests, head rest and footplate. The adapted chair fits into a complementary set with junior and adult options which eliminate any feelings of exclusion. They all share the same distinctive stainless-steel frame and easy-wash, removable memory foam cushions with a contemporary look and feel.

Alexander Burgess
Product Design BSc

Moments

A companion service aimed at improving the mental well-being of those travelling solo through mindfulness interventions and self reflection techniques.

Moments acts as an assistant for leisure travellers embarking on a solo trip. Millions of people travel solo every year, however little consideration is given to how traveling solo can take its toll on both the travellers and their loved ones. Moments aims to intervene when users may be experiencing feelings of loneliness through meditation and self-reflection.

Moments targets the points where users may be experiencing these feelings through the use of a companion wristband. This tracks the user's heart rate and calculates their heart rate variability (HRV), a measure of the time intervals between heart beats, directly linked to stress levels. When it detects that their heart rate variability is lowering, the service intervenes through the mobile app.

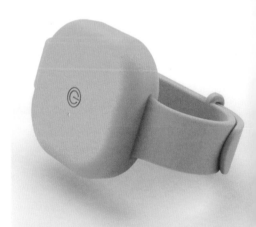

A collaborative project with Ignius Ltd

Peter Bushell
Product Design Engineering BSc

DeliveryBo

A collaboration with BotsAndUs to produce a system to allow their existing platform to fulfil a role performing indoor delivery.

This robot is designed to deliver products to people in an indoor space. It can autonomously navigate around it's environment, avoid static and dynamic obstacles and can transport large payloads to people in a secure compartment. It features a 7" touch screen with a fully interactive user interface allowing people to talk to the robot and have it reply or interact via the touch screen.

DeliveryBo has been developed with airport terminals in mind, offering passengers remote access to the retail facilities and restaurants from lounges or their gates. With a capacity of 30L and a top speed of 1.5m/s, it is ideally suited to efficiently deliver a variety of items and products bringing more convenient access to the facilities offered in an airport; consequently, boosting their profits.

A collaborative project with BotsAndUs

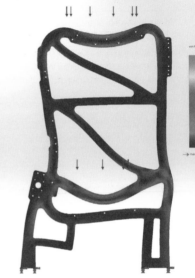

Samuel Bušovský
Industrial Design and Technology BA

Kalos

An audio-visual device which delivers relaxation sessions which prevent burn-out in employees. Its functionality is based on complementary and alternative medicine, neuroscientific and psychological approaches.

This audio-visual device encompasses an infinity mirror in the shape of a square frustum which produces kaleidoscopic images. The unique illusions which are produced through the infinity mirror effect, ferrofluid interaction with electromagnets and illumination, follow CAM (complementary and alternative medicine), neuroscientific and psychological approaches. The 10-minute structured relaxation session dissociates and entrains the user, allowing them to disengage with rumination of thoughts and the challenges of daily life while subconsciously training their focus and attention. The user also develops a better stress management response, creativity flow, and feels more relaxed overall after using the product. Furthermore, the attention focusing practise results in a greater ability at achieving flow states which are vital in the workplace and can then be applied to other aspects of the user's daily life.

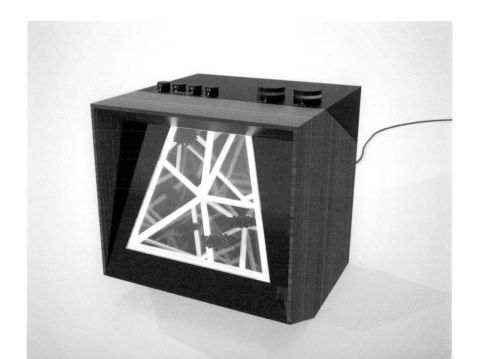

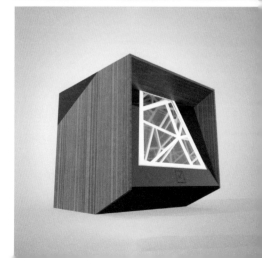

Imogen Campbell-Heanue
Product Design Engineering BSc

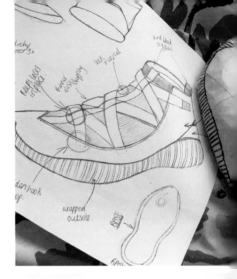

Nueva

An athletic shoe created specifically to prevent the occurrence of Patellar Tendonitis in female netball players, one of the most prevalent netball-related injuries.

In the ever-increasing female sporting world, it is evident that there is a considerable lack of design development, as seen with the current design of the athletic shoe. This is particularly concerning as there is a higher incidence of injury amongst female athletes. With netball becoming increasingly popular, it is more important now than ever that these athletes are protected, which is where Nueva comes into play.

Nueva is not only the first netball shoe aimed specifically at preventing Patellar Tendonitis, but it simultaneously works as a correctional shoe, encouraging muscle and strength development as well as improving posture.

Most importantly, the ground-breaking feature of Nueva is its design and development of the first known women's athletic shoe sole created purely based on the anatomical measurements and features of a woman's foot.

Arun Chalotra
Industrial Design and Technology BA

Ora

A sustainable and decorative material made up of seaweed (macroalgae) for indoor applications, combating health and environmental issues with current indoor building materials.

Current indoor building materials pose many problems to the occupants of the indoor environment. These materials contribute heavily to poor indoor air quality through the emission of VOCs (volatile organic compounds). They also combine toxic chemicals and materials from a highly unsustainable source and manufacturing process, causing considerable environmental impact.

Ora utilises the health, environmental and aesthetic benefits of the seaweed organism to create a versatile material application in the indoor environment. The material is solvent free, emits zero VOCs and is environmentally responsible, creating a superior alternative to current building materials. It is made up of sSeaweed, an eco-friendly/non-toxic binder and sealant.

Through bringing nature indoors, Ora engages with occupants on a biophilic and holistic level, thus improving human-nature relationships and aiming to enlighten attitudes towards a greener approach in the built environment.

Shujie Chen
Industrial Design and Technology BA

TIMEMARK

This project aims for people to develop a better reading habit through quantified self functions, to encourage users to read books regularly.

Nearly 60% of the world's population reads daily or more than once a week. 6% have never read books, which is equivalent to 22,000 consumers in 17 countries. Research indicates that only 51% of UK adults read, with 34% of them reading more than ten books. Not to mention 41% of adults usually lie about the amount they read. Reading is an excellent behavioural habit to develop, although the population of people who read has decreased in the last few years.

TIMEMARK is a quantified reading device, developed to help people develop better reading habits with reminders and self-quantified functions. The device clips onto a book and marks the page with a string. Reading time can be accumulated and recorded to see how much reading was done. A reading reminder in the form of LED and sound will occur every day.

Yili Chen
Product Design BSc

Cervsmile

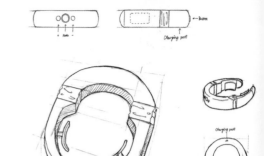

Cervsmile is a portable neck exercise reminder which is designed to prevent or alleviate neck problems in those with a sedentary lifestyle by reminding them to do neck exercises regularly.

Today, work and entertainment rely more and more on electronic devices. Most patients with neck problems have the experience of sitting and maintaining the same posture for a long time. Research indicates that a combination of neck exercises and stretching can help prevent the incidence of neck pain in office workers by approximately 50%; however, regular and adequate exercise is required to achieve the effect.

Cervsmile is designed to reduce neck problems by both prevention and alleviation. Neuromuscular Electrical Stimulation (NMES) causes muscles to contract by mimicking the action potential coming from the central nervous system. By applying NMES, the reminder will send electrical impulses to the user and their muscles will be stimulated at specified times to motivate them to do neck exercises. Two self-adhesive electrode pads used for the impulses can be removed for cleaning.

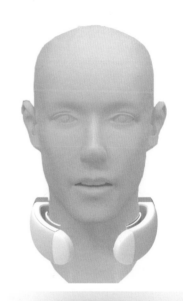

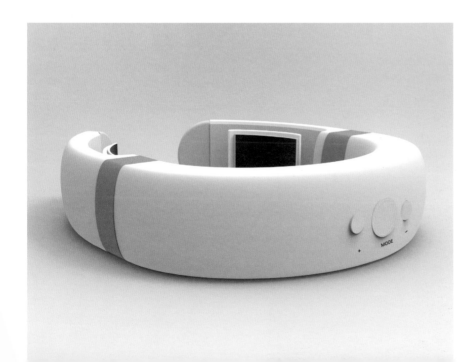

Niamh Cogley-Rock
Industrial Design and Technology BA

Urban Air

Unmasking the future, a personal air purifier, improving air quality for commuters in a global environment where there is an increasing need.

Air pollution kills 900 people every hour, with 9 million dying last year. Within the current market there is a lack of innovative designs tackling this worldwide epidemic.

Urban Air is a portable device which allows commuters to reduce their intake of harmful particles and consequently decrease their risk of developing an air pollution related illness. The device uses a motor powered by a rechargeable lithium battery to draw air through a HEPA filter. The direction of airflow is controlled through the nozzle; and the speed can be adjusted by turning the filter to meet the user's preference, environmental conditions or location. An OLED screen and LEDs provide real-time visual information. Maximum user comfort is ensured through the use of an internal gooseneck mechanism which allows unlimited shapes to suit any individual.

Hannah Coombs
Industrial Design and Technology BA

Get a Grip!

A set of products to make daily tasks easier for 50-70 year olds with dexterity-related impairments, positioned to challenge the stigma surrounding disabilities.

This project aims to empower users living with conditions such as arthritis, helping them perform everyday tasks and improving their independence. 'Get a Grip!' is a home hub containing three devices, that help with the following tasks: assisting with squeezing bottles (e.g. shampoo bottles), converting a top button into an easier side-squeeze (e.g. spraying deodorant) and opening packaging easily, even when out and about (e.g. food packaging).

The name 'Get a grip!' was born out of primary research, using humour and embodying the attitude of the user group, who are keen to carry on with normal life regardless of their limited dexterity. The tag-line, 'for young people who have lived a while', came directly from a user quote, epitomising the user group's desire to stay independent and avoid seeming 'old', whilst also remaining upbeat.

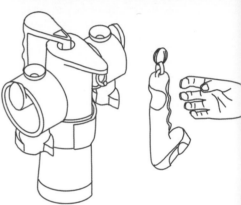

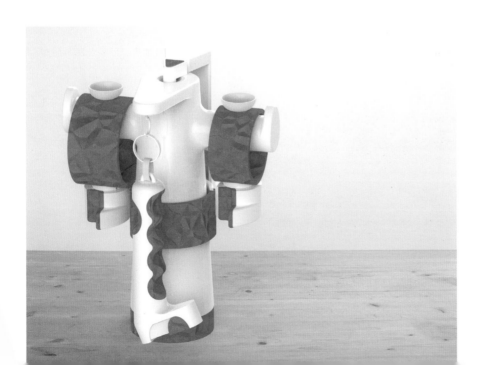

Pippa Copeland
Product Design BSc

Supporting New Dads

Improving the wellbeing of families by supporting men in becoming Dad: A suite of products to improve the bond between father and child.

Encouraging men to have a key role during pregnancy and after birth not only supports mothers but also improves a child's development outcomes. Improvements in the wellbeing of UK families through the social support fathers can provide could reap significant economic benefits to society - to the tune of £16.2 billion.

The strength of the project was the identification of a huge gap in current policies and products in the 'Mother and Baby' market to effectively support men to be involved as they become a Dad. A guided journal uses positive psychological interventions to improve the father's mental wellbeing and empowers them in the development of a bond with their child using storytelling. An app allows the father to record stories which can be played to the child even when the father is away.

Harry Cozens
Industrial Design and Technology BA

Fungal Grown Coffin

Applying the natural growing properties of mycelium in funeral design to produce a biomass coffin solution based on the principles of a circular materials economy.

As shifting social and political agendas challenge us to make more concerted efforts to be responsible for our natural environment, more and more people are looking for ways in which to make their own death more sustainable.

The objective of this project was to take an experiment-led approach to using mycelium as an alternative coffin making material. In nature, Mycelium helps to break down previously spent matter and release valuable nutrients back into the ecosystem. As a coffin material, this means it has the potential to not only reduce the environmental toll of extraction, but also make a positive contribution to the geosphere at the end of its product life. The final model shows the result of allowing a mycelium bio-composite mass to grow within a mould to produce an organic and sustainable coffin solution.

A collaborative project with Giraffe Innovation

Shivy Das
Industrial Design and Technology BA

Natural Detail

Creating custom footwear components in Timberland stores using a modular mould and algae-based sustainable material.

Natural Detail uses an algae-based polymer in Timberland footwear to reduce the environmental impact of its materials. Algae is a sustainable, versatile and fast-growing resource, and combats the issue of using land and food crops presented by conventional starch-based bioplastics. This material is cast in-store by the user for a custom fit, personalised aesthetic with different colours and patterns, and a unique user experience. Standardised width and length measurements determine the shoe size. For a custom fit, the instep (height) of the feet is also measured and categorised into a low, mid or high instep. These measurements and the foot size of the user can all be adjusted within the modular mould. Once the material is cast and dried, it is perforated around the edged to fix into the boot with popper buttons in the lining.

A collaborative project with Timberland

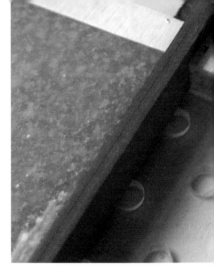

Angharad Davies
Product Design BSc

!Xu

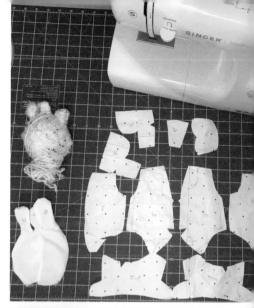

!Xu is a sterilisable and therapeutic soft toy, book and overarching system designed to help children understand and cope throughout their hospital stay.

Using a co-design method with patients and clinicians from Evelina London Children's Hospital, !Xu was designed to provide companionship and comfort to paediatric inpatients from admission through to post-discharge. By providing each child with a sterilisable cuddly toy that matches their hospital journey, !Xu is able to provide comfort, increase understanding and therefore reduce stress; these factors have been clinically proven to speed up healing.

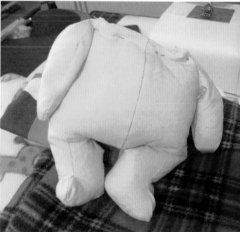

Stickers can be added to the toy to mimic conditions faced by children, and pages added to the book to show the toy undergoing the same procedures as the child. Each toy can be cleaned using current NHS sterilisation techniques to ensure infection control criteria are maintained. The current global pandemic has highlighted to us just how necessary the prevention of infection is, and !Xu enables safe play for your child.

A collaborative project with Guy's and St.Thomas' NHS Foundation Trust

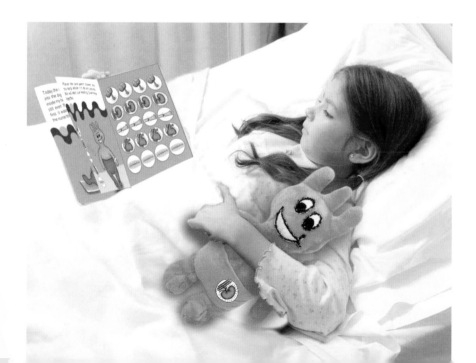

Jack Day
Industrial Design and Technology BA

Tea-Pots

Tea-Pots are sustainable, durable and compostable plant pots created from recycled waste teabags sealed in a sustainably sourced, waterproof beeswax shell.

In the UK half a billion petrochemical plant pots end up in landfill every year. These pots take around 5 lifetimes to bio-degrade, releasing harmful chemicals during their eventual breakdown. Every day in the UK, 100 million cups of tea are consumed: 98% are made with a tea bag which are often thrown into general waste; again, destined for landfill.

The aim of the Tea-Pots project is to take this already imported waste material (tea bags) combined with sustainably sourced, biodegradable beeswax to create fully sustainable, durable and compostable plant pots. The chemicals within the beeswax allow the pots have a lifetime decided by the consumer, as breakdown will not occur until such a time as the pot is entered into a composting environment. The eventual aim of the project is to replace plastic plant pots altogether.

Coleman Deady Ridge
Industrial Design and Technology BA

Athru

Athru is an adaptive luminaire that can provide a range of excellent lighting to match the changing needs of users and living spaces.

Research has shown that, more than ever, residents are using their living spaces for a wider variety of activities. A static lighting setup, which many people have in their homes, has been shown not to be able to accommodate this breadth of activities, thus adaptive lighting is necessary.

Athru can alter the illumination, colour temperature and direction of light it produces to create a wide breadth of lighting that might best support the variety of activities performed in our living spaces.

Additionally, Athru can be controlled simply using one industry standard dimmer switch. The use of this enables truly intuitive user interaction and allows for a relatively simple installation process.

Athru uses a modern aesthetic language and is designed to be attractive and complimentary to a space without being obtrusive or clashing with a user's personal style.

Chris Delaney
Industrial Design and Technology BA

Carapeis

Carapeis Body Armour is a breathable, lightweight and modular personal protection solution for young men in high-risk professions, such as private security or bodyguards.

This project involved extensive research of a chronic national problem: knife crime. On the rise since 2014, it is currently at its highest since comparable records began.

Largely caused by severe cuts to the UK police force as well as significant reductions to youth services, this problem is a double-edged sword with young men making up the majority of both victims and suspects.

Carapeis offers those in high-risk professions in the private sector an opportunity to utilise their training due to their personal, customised protection experience. The armour uses a lightweight, breathable vest with strategic attachment points for specially designed armour pads. The vest is given structure by the Kevlar straps, while the pads are made from stab-proof UHMWPE and D3O foam for improved impact resistance.

Miles Egbuchiem
Industrial Design and Technology BA

Versal Treadmill

A treadmill console designed to address the lack of accessibility in fitness equipment for visually impaired users, through utilizing improved audio output and tactile controls.

Currently physical inactivity in the visually impaired community is all too common, with a major cause being the increasing inaccessibility of fitness equipment currently available in gyms and health clubs across the country. Versal looks at how modern fitness equipment can be rethought to increase usability for visually impaired users through designing a treadmill console that leverages the benefits of improved audio output and tactile interaction.

Simplified analogue controls allow the users to easily adjust the workout to their preferences, while also providing Bluetooth compatible audio description that aids users in navigating through the digital interface while also updating them with real-time fitness metrics. Along with this the digital interface can be adapted to increase visibility and users can access previous workout data through pairing their phone with the treadmill through the app.

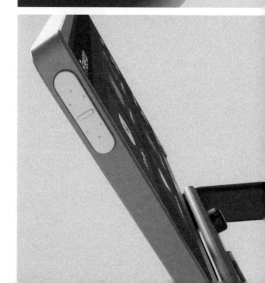

George Farren
Product Design Engineering BSc

Automating Saffron

An autonomous picking system which utilises computer vision to roam a field of Saffron flowers, identify flowers in bloom, home in and extract their three stigmas, largely without human input.

Saffron is the most expensive crop in the world and is hugely labour intensive to harvest. It is the dried stigma of the Crocus Sativus flower, and is extremely delicate, so requires hand picking, with hundreds of thousands of flowers needed to produce 1 kilogram of saffron. The drone uses computer vision to identify saffron flowers in bloom, then homes in on them and uses its compliant gripper to grab each stigma, before sucking them up into its holding chamber with the onboard fan. When low on battery, it returns to the hub, where it deposits saffron into the main drying chamber, and wirelessly recharges on the outer pad. The main hub monitors the drones' movement, offloading some computing, and keeping track of their status. The exhaust heat from the hub's computer is used to dry the collected saffron.

A collaborative project with Digital Kinematics

Justine Fernandez
Product Design Engineering BSc

Pulse

Sleep is a vital part of our everyday lives but for people who suffer from fibromyalgia, a condition that causes chronic pain, it can be difficult to get enough.

Fibromyalgia affects approximately 1 in 20 people. Unfortunately, sufferers are commonly subjected to suspicion, rejection, and disbelief from onlookers and some healthcare professionals because of the invisible nature of the symptoms. With no cure, patients are forced to live with the chronic pain and other symptoms with few options at hand to help them cope. One of the most affected parts of their lifestyle is the ability to fall asleep and gain enough restorative rest.

Pulse utilises a 4-7-8 breathing exercise, using the sense of sight and touch to guide the user into a relaxed state. As they focus on the device's haptic reciprocating motion applied to the palm, or a soft pulse of light across the bedroom walls, the user is able to fall asleep at ease so they can wake up the next morning feeling refreshed.

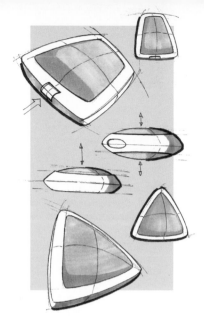

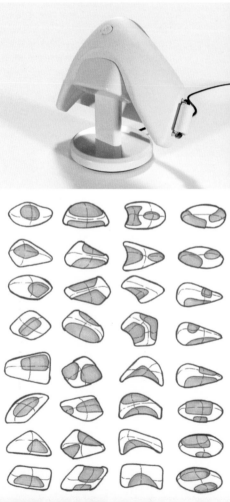

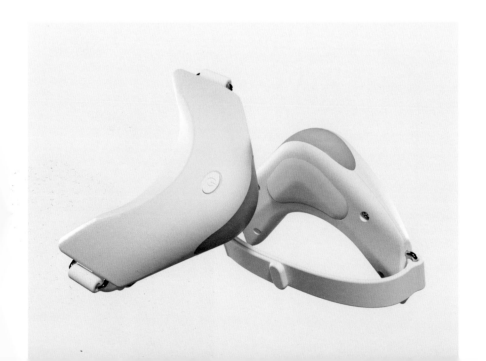

Elise Filleul
Industrial Design and Technology BA

Orion

Orion is an exercise product and app which enables patients with chronic muscular dystrophy diseases to enjoy working out in the knowledge that they are doing so efficiently and safely.

Exercise improves the baseline function for those with muscle weakness conditions, drastically improving their quality of life. However, the patient's access and adherence to physiotherapy are poor - they find it boring or forget to do it. Orion tackles this by connecting the patient with a specialist physiotherapist via the app for a consultation. The physiotherapist then creates a specialist workout to help the patient meet their goals.

Orion has a sensor and weights which can be attached to the torso, arms and legs. The weights are each 100g allowing up to 400g load in each location on the body. The Orion app syncs with the dock to play the user's choice of music and to give instructions to improve technique. The sensor tracks their movements to monitor technique, progress their work-out and detect if their condition is worsening.

A collaborative project with UCB Pharmaceuticals

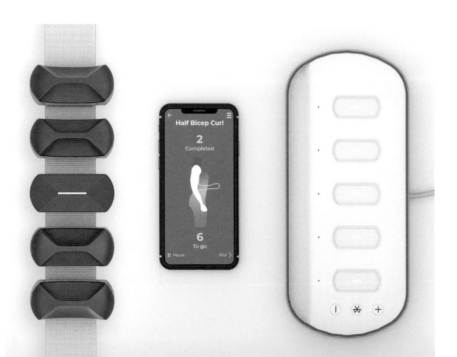

Robert William Foulds
Industrial Design and Technology BA

Parametric Tailoring

This product-service system uses parametric design to facilitate the competitive mass production of tailored, high performance rock climbing shoes.

Tailored footwear is necessary for rock climbers to have optimal contact with the wall. Currently, climbers acquire a tailored fit by breaking in shoes, a process of squeezing their feet into shoes often four sizes too small. Moulding the shoes to their feet causes pain and discomfort and also causes foot deformities.

'Parametric Tailoring' is a product-service system that manipulates 3D scans of users' feet using recorded biometrics on how their feet move dynamically. The system then builds the shoe around these manipulated scans and output the shoe manufacture plan. The process is entirely automated meaning both the cost and the lag time from order to delivery are reduced, two major sticking points of current handmade tailored climbing footwear.

A collaborative project with The North Face

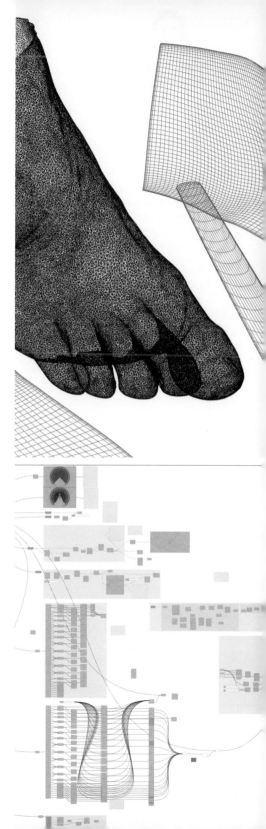

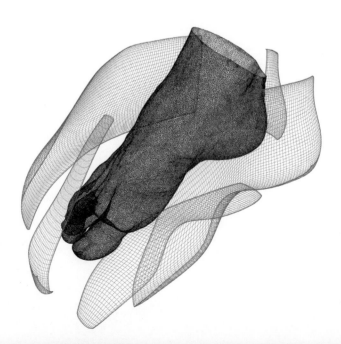

Angus Galton
Industrial Design and Technology BA

BioSphere

A multi-sense stimulating product that uses the benefits of plants to improve the time we spend indoors whilst working at a desk or workstation.

Humans are becoming ever more disconnected from nature. As populations flock to cities and work longer hours, this disconnect is only expected to increase. The average person spends more than 90% of their waking hours indoors. 1/3 of this time is spent working, normally idol, at a desk. This causes people to experience a lack of sunlight, fresh air, movement, sensory stimulation and nature. As humans have an innate connection to nature, this starvation from the outside world is more dangerous than we realise. It effects our health, performance, and mood.

Plants can be placed inside, but space quickly becomes an issue. This is where Biosphere comes in. A space efficient, sense stimulating, easy to maintain and beautifully designed rotating plant pot, perfect for any desk, workstation, or home office.

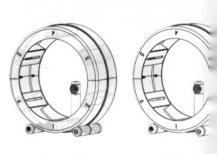

Andrew Gardner
Industrial Design and Technology BA

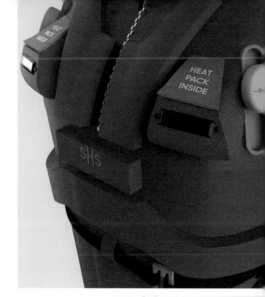

Sammy Suit

The Samoyed Hypothermia Suit (known as the Sammy Suit) makes it possible to treat hypothermia in extreme pre-hospital locations using active external rewarming.

Hypothermia, if not treated swiftly, can be fatal. When exposed to extreme cold weather conditions the chances of developing hypothermia are very high and exposure often occurs in remote, difficult to reach locations. Last year, over 25% of all casualties rescued by the RNLI (Royal National Lifeboat Institute) from UK waters were suffering from hypothermia. Currently the most efficient treatments are found in hospital and only passive external treatments, for example, blankets are available for use at the rescue location.

The Samoyed Hypothermia Suit effectively treats hypothermia with active external rewarming at the point of rescue. The Sammy Suit uses chemical heat packs that are easily activated providing a safe rewarming heat source that helps stabilize and increase the body temperature thus giving the casualty a better chance of survival.

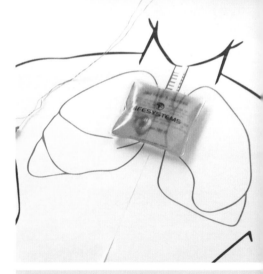

Matt Gardner
Product Design Engineering BSc

AWaRe

AWaRe offers an Autonomous Waste Removal solution to tackle the increasing problem of plastic pollution in the UK canal network.

In 2019, 14 million pieces of plastic were removed from in and around UK canals. Once plastic has entered the slow-moving water of the canals, it is difficult for volunteers to remove. Thus, the plastic remains in the water, to degrade into microplastics and negatively affect the biomass of the ecosystems.

This project has developed a solution which provides the autonomous collection of plastic waste. The device travels up the canal network, using a camera to analyse the canal bank, where plastics are identified by utilising colour analysis technology suitable for a raspberry Pi. Once identified, the collection cycle is triggered, the device then moves towards the plastic. A capture bucket is then submerged into the water, using the inflow of water to capture the waste, before being extracted and emptied into the waste storage hopper.

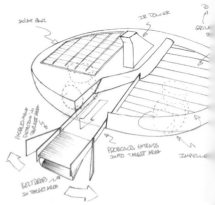

Sirtaj Singh Ghata-Aura
Industrial Design and Technology BA

VUI

Visual Unit Indicator - A visual lighting device that informs drivers of vehicles on the road with self-driving assists.

VUI is a dash camera with an integrated visual lighting indicator aimed at vehicle commuters that have self-driving assisted vehicles. Its purpose is to inform both drivers and road users if the vehicle is driving with autonomous assist functions and alert them in cases of emergency when failure occurs.

The product has three main functions using its visual indicator LEDs which help increase awareness; providing information if the user is setting the self-driving parameters, if the system is active and working, or if the system has failed and the user is no longer in control. The LED ring displays different colours based upon the vehicle status, glowing turquoise when using assists or flashing purple when it fails.

Charlie Gilks
Product Design Engineering BSc

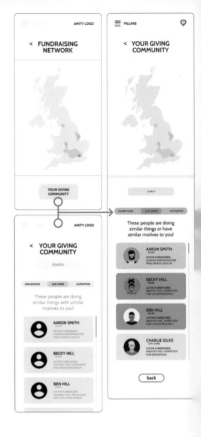

Virtue

Elevating the way people fundraise through four essential tools brought together in a single mobile platform, helping those with little free time to make a difference.

People aged 20-40 find it difficult to immerse themselves in raising money for worthy causes due to the demands of building careers and families. This can lead to unfamiliarity with the emotional rewards of altruism and selflessness through individual action.

Virtue is a service designed to aid an individual's fundraising journey, whatever form it takes, through a combination of time management and fundraising engagement tools that are tailored to the person and their specific needs. The ability for users to combine their crowdfunding means, all of their fundraising logistics, sharing their journey with others through any digital medium and creating a community of like minds makes for the most complete fundraising experience. This in turn helps foster a culture of giving amongst the younger generations through forming long-term links with the causes that they personally identify with.

Sam Harding
Product Design Engineering BSc

Fej

Fej is a system for creating custom-fitted aerodynamic cycling helmets from 3D scans, maximising rider performance by fitting all aspects of the helmet optimally to the rider's body.

Fej is the result of conversations between team-mates and competitors throughout the 2019 race season, discussing recent innovations within the sport of cycling and how the current rules could be pushed and bent in the pursuit of performance gains.

Applying recent developments in approaches to cycling aerodynamics with the use of anthropometrics from 3D scans and CFD testing, a design process was created allowing for the rapid creation of designs for custom-fitted racing helmets that integrate into the rider's body allowing for optimum performance against aerodynamic drag. Insights gathered during research found promising applications of machine learning in similar applications within aerospace, currently in the research stage. With proper development, an AI-based design process for helmets could produce better performing helmets for a wider range of users with fewer requirements for manual design work, refining the design process with each helmet.

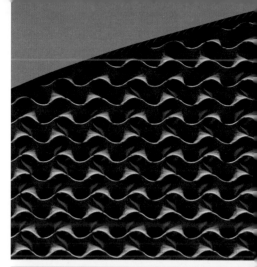

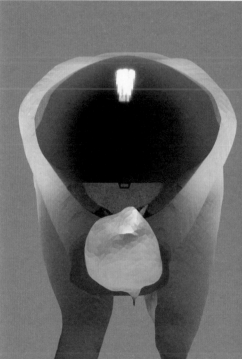

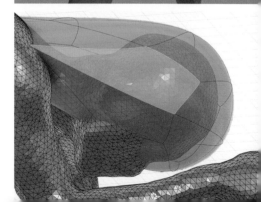

Evelyn Grace Harris
Product Design BSc

Bloom.

Bloom has been designed to allow older adults over the age of 65 years who live alone to grow herbs, microgreens and sprouts indoors.

Many older adults struggle with finding motivation to cook, or don't know many easy meals to cook from scratch. By growing their own produce, the user gains a sense of pride from being able to cook with food they have grown by themselves and are more likely to incorporate fresh food into their diet.

As age increases, appetite can decrease - this means that nutrient-dense meals are more important than ever. Produce like microgreens and sprouts are packed full of nutrients, providing its consumer with a high amount of vitamins and minerals even in a small portion. Nature is known to have many physical and mental benefits for people. Even just a few minutes with a plant can have a positive effect on cognitive function.

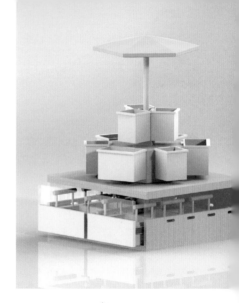

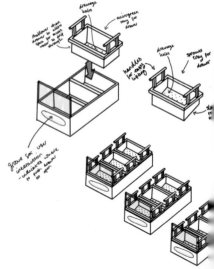

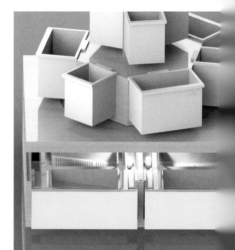

Amin Haruna
Industrial Design and Technology BA

Solar Tree

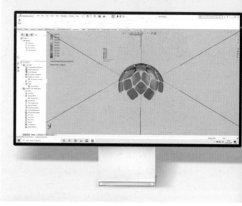

A Solar Tree that utilises biophilic design to generate solar power and provide a desirable urban space for members of the public.

Despite its merits, factors such as relatively high prices, variability in energy generation and visual clutter hinder the adoption of photovoltaic energy solutions. Solar photovoltaic technology also has issues with land requirement, especially in urban areas where land is a premium commodity, as well as its public perception because of its disruptive and imposing look.

The Solar Tree aims to address these issues by eliminating the visual clutter often associated with photovoltaics, and mitigating the variability of energy captured at different times of the day by emulating the natural characteristics of trees - all while reducing the land area required to harness solar energy. The Solar Tree also aims to foster a desirable urban space that is accessible, safe, legible and inclusive by providing amenities such as lighting, seating, charging ports and WiFi to members of the public.

A collaborative project with Solar Botanic

Georgina Hatch
Product Design Engineering BSc

Wave Warrior

Wave Warrior is a trans-tibial surfing prosthesis for children, with a tri-axial ankle, increased grip sole and modular system.

A minimal selection of prosthesis' are available to children, especially ones that would allow for the movement surfing requires.

Wave Warrior's ankle comprises two polyurethane rubber bushings that surround the leg post. The hardness of the rubber depends on the user's weight and allows for the leg post to flex multi-directionally. The system can be easily disassembled and modified; when the child grows, they can swap for a stiffer rubber bushing. An adjustable leg post can also be easily replaced for a longer post.

For increased grip, there are rubber sleeves on the toe and heel of a carbon fibre foot, curved edges for a larger surface area and more contact with the board when the foot is at an angle, and a split-toe recess creates a suction grip, inspired by the hooves of mountain goats.

Fatima Hermosin Acasuso
Product Design Engineering BSc

Flora

Flora is a hybrid riverboat solution powered by solar energy which promotes indigenous communities' development through a new means of transport.

Brazilian indigenous communities are the targeted customer for this project. Indigenous communities represent 15% of the world's poorest people. Most of the time, they are not able to fulfill their basic primary needs due to the high cost or simply lack of fuel in the remote areas where they live. The aim is to make transport feasible without fuel dependence.

The project has addressed three different areas. Firstly, improving the boat's range during the electric mode by evaluating different technologies to deliver the best performance at a reasonable price. Secondly, improving the mechanical performance by designing a clutch mechanism which disengages the diesel engine and transmits the electric motor's torque to the propeller shaft. And thirdly, a co-design activity with the user to understand their way of thinking and outline the project according to their knowledge, values and beliefs.

A collaborative project with Williams Advanced Engineering

Jesslin Ho
Product Design Engineering BSc

EMS Device

A retrofit device to accelerate wastewater treatment and electrofuel production, using Electro-Methanogenic Systems (EMS) developed by WASE to treat wastewater and generate biogas, fertilisers.

A collaboration with WASE, this project utilises their core technology to create a wastewater treatment device. EMS is the stimulation of microbial bacteria with electricity to speed up the anaerobic digestion of waste and production of methane fuel. The aims are to increase the efficiency of pre-existing household and community decentralised wastewater, maximise current assets and resource recovery.

When organic waste is digested and broken down in an environment with no oxygen, anaerobic digestion takes place. High nutrient organic matter and bio-gas is produced and can be collected for use as fertilizer and fuel to generate electricity or heating.

In order to create a low-cost wastewater treatment solution a device containing the core components of the EMS can be used. It is a deployable structure which can be installed in common wastewater tanks to upgrade its function.

A collaborative project with WASE

Joseph Irvine
Product Design Engineering BSc

Award Winner
Most Innovative
Project

Scan a Scale

A faster produce purchasing system to encourage UK supermarket consumers to purchase more loose produce, reducing the use of plastic packaging with fresh produce.

Many of the UK's supermarkets are increasing the amount of loose produce available in stores to reduce their plastic packaging usage. Purchasing plastic-packaged fresh produce is far more convenient than purchasing the loose counterparts, opposing the convenience-based shopping mentality.

The Scan a Scale device is designed to improve the convenience of purchasing loose produce, integrating with the existing 'Scan and Go' supermarket shopping systems to reduce the use of plastic packaging. The paired scanner and scale devices allow shoppers to scan product barcodes and place produce directly into their bags hooked onto the scales on the back of the trolley, which weighs and prices items on the go. Shoppers can pay and leave without ever needing to use in the in-aisle scales, or unload their trolley at the checkout.

Waitrose were not engaged in any consultancy or collaborative capacity with this project. Any publicity is limited to personal, academic use.

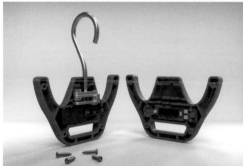

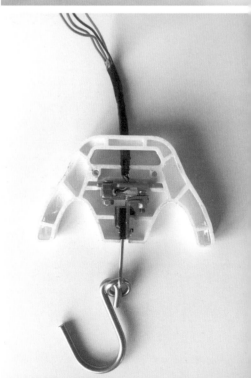

Jonathan James
Product Design Engineering BSc

TRUETRAY

A manufacturing system which empowers businesses to create their own fully-customised packing trays for one-off product shipments.

Moulded pulp trays have been extensively used when transporting mass-produced consumer products. Now, with the use of TRUETRAY, the advantages of these packing trays can be applied to one-off products such as 3D printed parts and artisan ceramics.

This counter-top manufacturing system creates ready-to-ship moulded pulp trays, each uniquely fitted to their cargo in as little as 15 minutes. Packers can select from a range of tray mould sizes with deformable Lycra centres to suit a range of applications. The mould and shipped product are placed into the unit where the automated system creates a pulp tray from a paper slurry. The use of form-fitted moulded pulp trays greatly reduces the number of ways in which a parcel can be improperly packed; thereby reducing the severity and frequency of cargo damage.

Jan Nicholas Janiurek
Industrial Design and Technology BA

DynamicDesignProcess

A new system to create custom bicycle geometry without the need for a bike fit process, enabling builds without face-to-face requirements.

The Dynamic Design Process, or DDP, is a system created in collaboration with the company I started on my entrepreneurial placement year, Ember Cycles. The system takes some design ideas from a completely custom built bicycle process and some ideas from mass manufactured frames. The outcome allows for the creation of custom bicycle frames without using expensive, time-consuming methods.

By designing an 'ideal' frame solution for the 50th percentile human, adaptations can be made to fit a range of sizes, from 1st to 100th percentile to the frame geometry. Then, by allowing for the difference in size in relation to geometry, such as a smaller person having a fewer degrees in a head angle and a larger person having more degrees, each frame can feel like the ideal geometry, no matter the person riding it.

A collaborative project with Ember Cycles

Viraj Javaharlal
Product Design BSc

Budget Buddy

A fun and engaging budgeting tool designed for children between the ages of 8-11. Budget Buddy helps children manage their money and understand its value in the digital age.

As this world is shifting towards digital means of payment, children find it increasingly more difficult to contextualise money and truly understand the importance of it. Recent studies confirm that financial habits acquired at a younger age are likely to influence important decisions made in the future.

Budget Buddy is a response to these concerns of financial management in the digital age. Buddy simplifies budgeting into 3 key categories: Saving, Spending and Sharing. Children earn money through 'Money Missions' that enforce good behaviours, the missions and rewards being set and tracked by the parents using the app. Buddy's large display can be used by the children to track their money and view short stimulating videos intended to communicate proper money management and deciding where to store money.

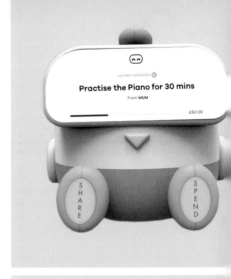

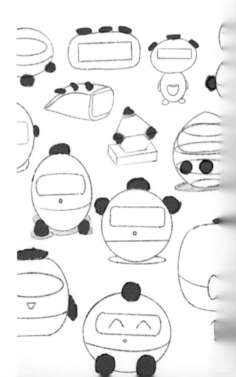

Elias Kara
Industrial Design and Technology BA

Safe Way Bag

Protecting individuals from knife crime in the UK by studying how it is impacting civilians and what needs to be done to minimise its effects.

Public safety is the number one priority of governments and law enforcement agencies - keeping the community protected and served is crucial. At present civilians have no real way to defend themselves or keep themselves safe against attacks with a knife or sharp instrument.

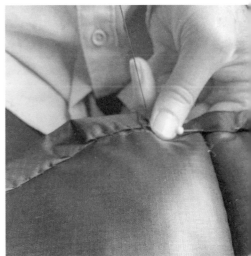

The Safe Way Bag protects civilians against knife attacks. This product is a fashionable, reasonably priced garment suitable for all. It is accompanied by a phone application that offers a safe way to any location (avoiding high crime areas), an alert system for the police, a contact section and a shop to purchase the accompanying products. The product features a Kevlar element, resulting in an accessory that is discrete, undercover and inconspicuous.

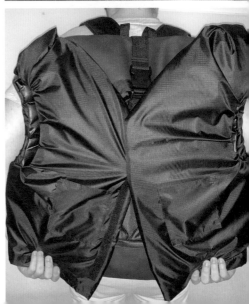

Megan King
Industrial Design and Technology BA

Inhilate

Inhilate is a nebuliser mask designed specifically to reduce pressure on emergency healthcare professionals by allowing them to deliver emergency oxygen therapy to patients quickly and effectively.

The demand for UK ambulance services has been growing on average by 5% a year for a decade. Existing inefficiencies in equipment are being highlighted due to the pressure on emergency healthcare professionals to deliver the same level of exceptional care to many more patients in a shorter space of time. Professionals that deliver life saving services everyday should not have to adapt to equipment inefficiencies.

Inhilate is an emergency nebuliser mask used to deliver medication in the form of a vapour to treat respiratory conditions. Inhilate focuses on resolving pain points that were identified by emergency healthcare professionals themselves, to make the medication process as easy and efficient as possible. The product allows patients to be efficiently treated in any position and medication to be dispensed into the chamber quickly and safety via the delivery chute.

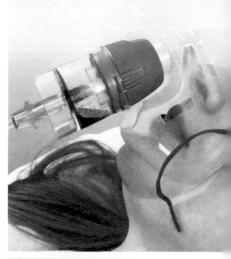

Thomas Knipe
Industrial Design and Technology BA

Illumitrex

Illumitrex is a smart survival tool that generates electricity as you walk, charges mobile phones and powers a torch to help aid in an emergency situation.

Illumitrex is a device that will generate energy as you walk for hikers and campers. The device is equipped with a built-in generator, torch and USB-C charger for mobiles. Designing the product as a smart survival tool aims to push the product into the hiking market. To aid the user, Illumitrex will charge phones if they are low on battery to call emergency services and light up dark areas with the built-in torch.

By using Faraday's Law, the device is capable of generating electricity through kinetic motion via an inductor. The power is then stored in a 7200mAh Li-ion battery that will charge two phone batteries along a journey. The power can then be distributed to the torch and USB-C charger.

Tanaka Kungwengwe
Industrial Design and Technology BA

Sana Health

Sana is a rehabilitation management system consisting of a mobile and wearable application designed to improve long-term post-operative outcomes for patients undergoing ACL reconstruction recovery.

ACL ruptures account for 50% of all sports-related knee injuries, 76.6% of which result in reconstruction surgery, necessitating long-term patient rehabilitation. To ensure optimal recovery and reduce the chances of secondary knee osteoarthritis, patients must remain compliant with treatment and perform exercises correctly.

The Sana system is the first of its kind, consisting of a mobile and wearable application that adopts behavioural design principles and gamification theory to improve long-term post-operative outcomes for ACL reconstruction recovery. The system allows users to: assess quality (i.e., measure the quality of adherence to exercise instructions at a specific time), monitor performance (i.e., measure performance by monitoring the quality of a pre-determined set of exercises over time) and share data (i.e., share performance data periodically with clinicians, helping them make well informed and timely treatment decisions).

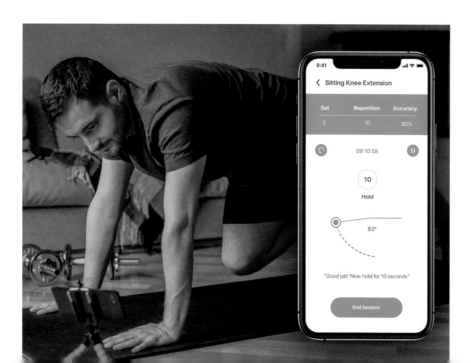

Oliver Lambert
Industrial Design and Technology BA

Vans Haptics

Through haptic feedback (communication through vibration), Vans Haptics provides technique correction for Snowboarders in real-time; significantly reducing learning periods and developing one's understanding of how their technique can improve.

This is Vans Haptics. Designed to enhance your snowboarding ability, this performance band tracks and analyses your technique to provide real-time, technique correcting feedback. Wirelessly connected to embedded pressure sensors in the insole, this product analyses your body positioning and weight distribution alongside the motion capture sensors in the core unit. It is designed for amateur and intermediate Snowboarders looking to improve their technique in real-time without the need for external observation, seeking to develop a user's understanding of how to improve and significantly reducing the time required to learn and develop skills.

With the assistance of an app, users can watch their performance playback and track their technique progression as their activity data is automatically linked to the Vans Haptics App.

Skyler Riz Manalili
Product Design BSc

Trio

Transforming furniture designed for small living spaces within urban cities, while providing an environment for friends and family to disconnect from the digital world and socially reconnect face to face.

In recent years London's population has significantly increased, where there were 8.8 million people in 2016, it is estimated to rise to 9.3 million in 2021. With this, more high-density living spaces are being developed within urban cities to provide homes for the increasing population. However, the issue arises in the limit of space to move around, possibly due to furniture overcrowding problems in small homes, therefore, leaving little room to move.

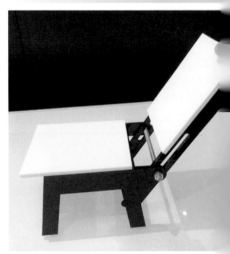

The Trio is a piece of furniture designed to resolve this issue, by having two different configurations for different uses around the house, whether it be used as a coffee table, a single-seat chair, or a bench for two people during social gatherings. This project also tackles the issues of the digital world, taking over social interactions where people are more engaged with social media.

A collaborative project with Marta Abello

Oliver Martin
Industrial Design and Technology BA

Dual basket

Reducing water used in the laundry process by preventing over-washing, increasing efficiency and providing users with a greater awareness of the water crisis.

As lifestyles become more water-intensive and washing becomes more accessible, greater pressure is placed on rapidly-depleting water resources. With it estimated that 40% of clothes put in for wash are suitable to be worn again, there is a huge opportunity to save water by reducing the amount of clothes put in for wash unnecessarily.

The basket takes a holistic approach to the problem, by informing the user on the amount of water being used in their laundry process, allowing them to act responsively. The basket also notifies the user when they have enough laundry for a complete load - preventing underfilling and overfilling of the machine. Additionally, the supplementary app provides enhanced product functionality as users are able to view their habits in more detail, set targets and share wash loads with other dual basket users.

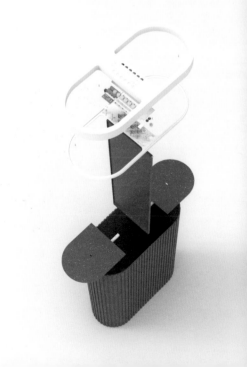

Preetpaul Matharoo
Product Design Engineering BSc

Healthy Home System

A human-centred smart-environment system, designed to optimise living conditions and reduce daily stresses through automation and monitoring services.

The Healthy Home System aims to tackle issues caused by poor home environments; offering comfort and security in a revitalising ambience. The system features four environmental systems that are controlled and monitored through a dedicated smart controller and not a downloadable app to avoid any possible security issues.

From research conducted around human circadian rhythms, the system is tuned to autonomously adjust lighting and temperature throughout the day; using sunlight mimicking interior lighting and dynamic temperature regulation. Smart capabilities enable the system to supply the user with specific environmental data such as air quality, utility usage by appliance and waste created. Additionally, notifications are sent updating the user on air quality issues and where efficiency improvements can be made. Specifically, for the Vistadais Off-Grid home; notifications also include when utility stocks are running low or have been restored.

A collaborative project with Vistadais

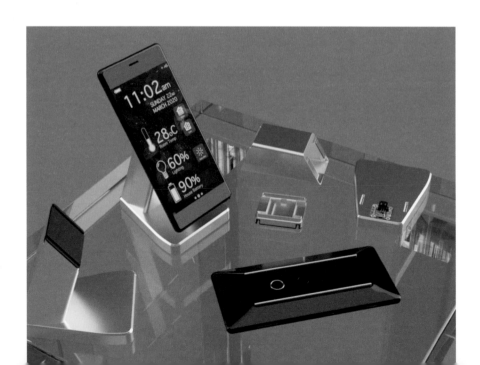

Jacob McAdam
Product Design Engineering BSc

Award Winner
Best of
Environmental

Solar Fruit Drying

Using solar drying to reduce post harvest losses for small holding farmers in Africa, in collaboration with Alvan Blanch Dev Co.

In Africa, 500 million smallholding farmers lose 15% of their income to post harvest food losses. This project aims to reduce these post harvest food losses through fruit drying. By drying the produce, the shelf life of the crop is greatly increased and the food is prevented from simply going to waste in storage. The smallholding farmers will be able to utilise the drying process when they have an excess of harvest, or produce which is too large, small or misshapen. The increased shelf life also enables the farmers to sell their produce when the market is suitable; this means a higher sales price and more control for the farmer. This project is a collaboration with Alvan Blanch, a world-leader in the crop processing sector and already well-established in Africa.

A collaborative project with Alvan Blanch Dev Co

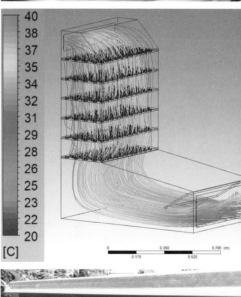

Stuart Meredith
Product Design Engineering BSc

ERO

Phase one of ERO is a Zero Waste shopping container that reduces user pain-points and increases the sustainability value when compared to current solutions.

The aim of this project is to provide a solution to Zero Packaging Shopping by making the process easier and more appealing to the consumer. The product must make the process accessible to new Zero Packaging Shopper whilst improving the current process for existing Zero Packaging Shopper. The environment and sustainability aspects are the core focuses of the project. After only four uses, ERO will have reduced your carbon footprint more than conventional single-use plastic packaging.

Phase one increases Zero Waste participation through designing user-focused containers, reducing the pain-points of the process. Phase two develops in-store service design in order to reduce touchpoints for the user, cutting down time spent collecting produce. Phase three aims to progress Zero Waste shopping to include delivery services through carbon-neutral vehicles, increasing accessibility for users.

Toby Middleton
Industrial Design and Technology BA

Hydra Templat

Removing the need to rely on instinct when trying to hydrate at the most efficient moments during a long-distance run.

Endurance runners currently have no method of measuring their hydration level whilst running long distances. While often overlooked, over hydration is just as dangerous as dehydration, which is why it is crucial to understand for both health and efficiency.

Hydra Templat calculates the runner's on-run sweat rate and notifies the user how much water they have lost, depending on a pre-set value. As the user maintains a constant pace during their run, their sweat rate will also remain the same. Contained within the headband is a small device which measures the moisture content on the user's forehead. Once calculated the data is sent to Hydra's app which notifies the runner - through sound or vibrations - of water lost during their run.

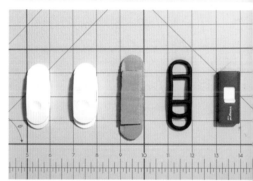

Oliver Minns
Industrial Design and Technology BA

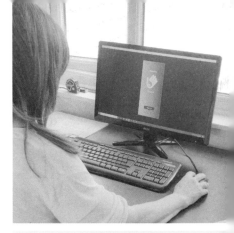

Hygienix

Hygienix is a system using gamification elements to encourage human behaviour change towards handwashing, reducing the spread of disease within heavily-populated buildings.

The spread of germs from public toilets is a silent epidemic, primarily down to the lack of personal hygiene practices within these environments. It's estimated that if everyone routinely washed their hands, a million deaths a year could be prevented as well as being able to reduce the risk of respiratory infections by 16%.

At the start of this project, no one could have seen the significantly-increased need and appeals for hand washing. As the Covid-19 pandemic impacts and changed the lives for so many, never has the need for a change to human handwashing practices been so important. Hygienix uses gamification elements to emulate competition and to motivate users into changing their hygiene practices.

Max Mitchell
Industrial Design and Technology BA

Ro

Ro is a multi-functional portable device that aims to improve the wellbeing of informal dementia caregivers through educational assistive technology.

Ro is an assistive device that aims to improve the wellbeing of informal dementia caregivers through education. Ro uses voice recognition software which allows the user to directly ask the device questions, resulting in immediate dementia related information. The device can retrieve dementia related information from trusted sources in the home or outside through its WiFi connection and 3G.

Ro's minimal, user-friendly features allow elderly users to interact with the product at ease; it has large buttons, a landscape screen for reading text as well as quick, bullet point answers. Ro is versatile; it has a navigation system if the user cannot hear or record the questions. To reach caregivers on low or no-income, Ro could be distributed through the NHS upon diagnosis of the person with dementia.

Roxana Mobasheri
Industrial Design and Technology BA

LIFEPILL

LIFEPILL is a medication adherence system designed to assist patients with increasingly complex pill regimes. It consists of a wearable smart patch, pill box and mobile application.

The Department of Health estimates that unused medicines cost the NHS £300 million every year. A major component of this medicine waste is caused by patient non-adherence. This is a passive process in which the patient may be careless or forgetful about adhering to their prescription treatment regimen. With almost half of all adults in the UK taking prescriptions daily, it can be hard to keep track.

LIFEPILL is a unique pill management system, that assists patients with long term health conditions, and those who would benefit from an assistive technology. LIFEPILL integrates a physical "pulse-like" reminder to the user, via a smart wearable patch that can be placed anywhere on the skin just like a plaster. It is paired to a mobile application via Bluetooth and relays signals according to the patients pill regime.

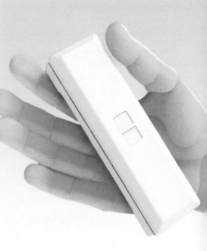

Anavi Modi
Product Design BSc

Respire+

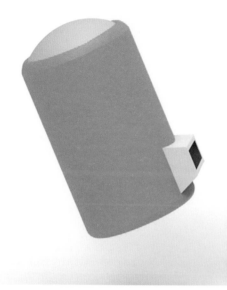

Respire+ is an asthma managing device developed for children to help them control asthma efficiently. This project aims to make asthma management an easy task.

Asthma is considered to the most common chronic disease in children and adolescents imposing a burden on the health care system. According to WHO, there is an estimated 300 million people who have asthma globally with an additional 100 million by 2025.

Respire+ aims to engage children with the use of an interactive screen that can measure duration, frequency, set reminders and monitor the inhaler dosage count. The inhaler uses a cylindrical shape to ensure that the product can be held firmly. There are two monitoring plates connected via Bluetooth. One of the monitoring plates is used to hold the inhaler, and the other is an interactive screen. The size and structure of the plates makes the product easy to carry and store.

Lewis Muggeridge
Industrial Design and Technology BA

Orbit

Orbit is a food assistant app that integrates with retailer information systems to provide the user with relevant meal suggestions based on their home inventory levels.

A third of all food produced is wasted, accounting for 8% of all global greenhouse emissions and nearly a trillion dollars in financial loss every year. The majority of food waste occurs in households and is mostly due to food not being eaten in time.

Orbit will help to reduce food waste by prioritising and suggesting recipes that use ingredients close to expiration. The app is powered by an inventory that tracks the consumption of food in the home. A new data input method was identified as an improvement to the current user experience, where the service would detect a purchase from a retailer and extract the latest shop data to automatically populate the user's inventory.

The overall aim of this app is to improve food-based knowledge and the understanding of the financial and environmental cost of food waste.

Nivedhaa Muthu
Product Design BSc

Bed Meal Table

A redesigned mealtime experience for bedbound patients in hospital wards across the country, affording greater access, independence and self-esteem.

Nutrition and food consumption in older adults decreases due to ageing, physical mobility and chronic illnesses. Around 44% of older patients are hospitalised long-term due to their health complications; consequently affecting their quality of life. Physical barriers around the patient's hospital bed deter access to the bedside table, causing increased dependence on nurses.

The proposed height-adjustable and cost-effective solution enables patients to eat independently at mealtimes. The bed meal table can be intuitively fitted onto the cot sides and allow immediate use, providing patients with greater access and control over their comfort. They can maintain a level of dignity and self-confidence during their hospital stay. The solution intends to have a profound impact on patients' independence and improve their food intake. This modular and inclusive design is safe to use, easy to clean and convenient to store.

A collaborative project with Guy's and St Thomas' NHS Foundation Trust

Jake O'Sullivan
Industrial Design and Technology BA

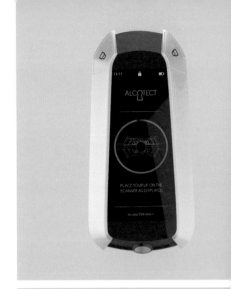

Award Winner
Most Disruptive
Project

Alcotect

The world's first vehicle key with a built-in breathalyser and biometric verification, preventing drink driving, keyless car thefts and uninsured driving.

The main aim of the project was to reduce the number of drinking related incidents on the road in a way that would also prevent car thefts and uninsured drivers. A change in EU legislation means all cars must be fitted with a breathalyser by 2022, as this year saw a 7% rise on alcohol related road accidents: the highest level since 2012.

Alcotect uses Biometric and Blood Alcohol Content (BAC) verification before allowing the user to enter their car through the use of a lip print scanner and alcohol sensor, preventing drivers from accessing the vehicle without the registered biometrics and a legal BAC reading. The key can be personalised to users' preferences through the selection of coloured inserts and options for the lock state progress displayed on the LCD.

Ruby Ovenden
Industrial Design and Technology BA

Extent

A service designed to reduce the negative environmental impacts of the UK music festival industry by educating attendees and allowing users to up-cycle their damaged tents.

Annually, the £2.6 billion UK festival industry creates an astonishing 23,500 tonnes of waste. With 3.17 million people in attendance, that is equal to 2.8 Kg per person daily which is over double the national rate. It is estimated that a large proportion of that waste is 250,000 abandoned tents.

The goal of this project is to introduce a service that educates the masses on the detrimental impact of excessive waste production and manufacturing. The service 'Extent' will allow attendees to donate their damaged tents onsite, by downloading the Extent app users can then track their tent as it is up-cycled into a range of new products. In doing so, users will be informed and educated, eventually accelerating the adoption of up-cycling and reducing the social sector's negative footprint.

David Paling
Product Design BSc

Bamboo Flatpack

A sustainable alternative to hardwood, softwood and traditional flatpack furniture. The product improves sustainability by reducing deforestation and improves user interaction by simplifying the assembly process.

This chair is produced from bamboo and so reduces the need for hardwoods and softwoods in the flatpack furniture industry. Bamboo is a renewable material which will quickly re-grow when harvested. Bamboo creates a strong and durable chair and is the only material used in the product.

The assembly process does not require any tools, fixtures or glue and uses only friction to hold the chair together. A simple wedge is placed into a slot underneath the backrest to fix the pieces in place. The user can choose to personalise their chair by adding painted areas to create a product with a modern and colourful finish unique to them. By extending the product's life span, strain on the environment is reduced and therefore the company focuses on sustainability in all aspects; promoting reuse, repair and recycling.

Arphatsara Paowana
Industrial Design and Technology BA

Tabi Friends

Assisting distressed preadolescents (8 - 12 years old) with sensory processing difficulties to feel calmer and more focused in the classroom or while travelling.

Sensory processing difficulties affect not only how children move and learn, but also how they play and interact with friends and especially how they view themselves. Tabi Friends comes in a range of collectable characters for the child to feel engaged with and comfortable to use when their sensory processing issues occur in public.

The product comprises of three main parts: A character appearing like a typical toy so as not to draw attention while in use, with a squeezable body to achieve deep pressure when feeling distressed, thus relieving anxiety. A weighted base to achieve pressure with ease and to encourage the child to move their arms (known as proprioception) while holding the toy, resulting in increased alertness and focus. Finally, a textured base cover for tactile relief to create a feeling of calmness.

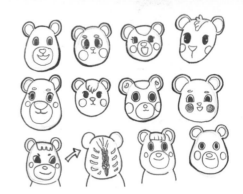

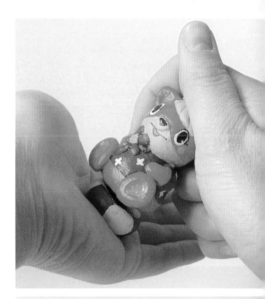

Seb Parker
Industrial Design and Technology BA

APACHI

APACHI is a system which provides respiratory protection for special operations users while integrating with ballistic combat helmets to decrease donning time and improve usability over existing helmet-mask solutions.

Special forces operatives need effective equipment to defend against current and emerging threats on the battlefield. Combat helmets provide ballistic and impact protection for wearers - hazards which are widespread in the field. Air Purifying Respirators are another essential form of protection against Chemical, Biological, Radiological or Nuclear hazards (CBRN) which may be less prevalent than projectiles but are still a high-risk threat. This means that ballistic and CBRN protection is needed and both helmets and respirators are often worn together. Currently, due to minimal integration, this creates issues with donning time, fitment and equipment compatibility.

APACHI (Air Purification And Combat Helmet Integration) is a system which provides seamless integration between combat helmets and air-purifying respirators. Donning time and ergonomics are improved by mounting a rigid respirator to the helmet with relocated filters.

A collaborative project with Avon Protection

Andrew Pickering
Industrial Design and Technology BA

Project Faber

Faber brings 3D printing of biodegradable footwear components into the retail environment, enabling personalised manufacture, sustainability-focused design and enhanced fit, all at the point of sale.

The project comprises two main parts, a bespoke 3D printing appliance and a modular footwear component. The printing appliance has been designed for operation in Timberland's flagship store. It includes integration of relevant branding and several functional aspects that differentiate it from other FDM printer appliances. Its dual extruder has been optimised for fast yet accurate material deposition, carried out within an airtight enclosure, which shields the user from particulates produced during operation.

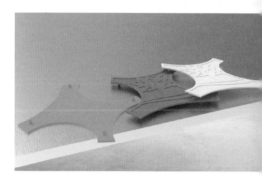

The flexible footwear component attaches to eyelets on Timberland's six-inch boot via snap-fits located on its underside. Each printed component is personalised to accommodate the customer's varying instep height, which increases both comfort and quality of fit. The printer uses a fully compostable filament, ensuring a circular life cycle and reducing the product's overall environmental impact.

A collaborative project with Timberland LLC

Maria Alejandra Pinilla Pease
Industrial Design and Technology BA

Share

Share aims to redefine the donation experience, creating deeper and stronger relationships between the charity and its donors through the power of storytelling and user-generated content.

Regaining public trust, remaining relevant in a competitive market, and embracing new technologies are the biggest challenges faced by charities. Therefore, charities need to rethink their donation strategies addressing the needs and expectations of their supporters.

Share is an interactive donation experience, which uses storytelling to connect charities and donors. The platform allows donors to understand how the charity's work makes a difference, and to stay connected with them. Users can explore stories and missions based on themes, treatments, or types of cancer, they can also create their own stories to share experiences and insights.

Share allows charities to experience continuous interaction with their donors, reaching a wider audience at any time or period of treatment. Through user-generated testimonials, stories in Share are unique and personal, and accurately showcase the charity's work.

A collaborative project with Guy's and St Thomas' NHS Foundation Trust

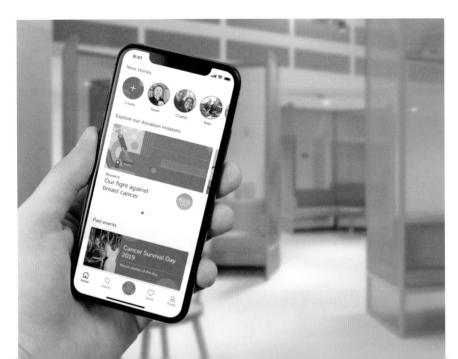

Jamie Pinkham
Product Design Engineering BSc

DX One

DX One is a health testing kit that provides quick and convenient testing, helping the family to stay fit and healthy.

The project was to design the product experience for a molecular diagnostic health testing kit and to develop a low-cost micropump to make it affordable for consumers. The product experience focused on meeting users' needs identified through primary research and safe use through following the In-Vitro Diagnostic Devices Directive (98/79/EC). A nozzle-diffuser micropump was developed using a metal-PDMS composite membrane as a more cost-effective alternative to silicon.

The digital tools available in the 21st Century have created the phenomenon of the quantified self where so much of our health and well-being can be measured and analysed; this level of instant information has led to an emerging demand for more convenient health diagnoses. In the context of the coronavirus pandemic, easy access to testing has become a necessity, not just a convenience.

A collaborative project with Decrypt DX

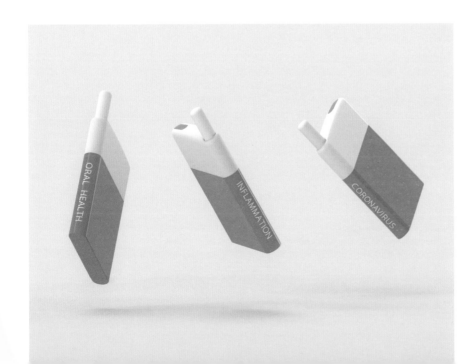

Victoria Poizer
Industrial Design and Technology BA

Thea

Thea is a menstruation service designed to reduce period poverty across the UK by educating women properly, creating a community among its users and encouraging giving to those in need.

Period poverty is the lack of access to safe and clean sanitary wear affecting 1 in 10 girls in the UK, Mainly due to poor education, financial hardship or physical constraints. Many sufferers miss school and often put their health at risk, which is why it is so important to make change now.

Thea provides guides for both parents and children to learn about menstruation and break down the stigma surrounding it. Users can sign up to the Iris box to receive regular parcels of sustainable period products, which can be upgraded to the Gaia box where users are delivered sustainable health, well-being and hygiene products on top of their regular menstrual items. Across the whole range of Thea products, for each item purchased one is sent to someone suffering from period poverty.

Katie Price
Industrial Design and Technology BA

derme

A patient-driven mobile app designed to provide adults self-managing a chronic skin condition with a greater sense of control and confidence.

Derme is the first remote solution to effectively and accurately help users track their condition over prolonged periods of time, by gathering and collating key data-sets about changes in the skin and it's impact on the user creating a more accurate picture of each individual. Derme also bridges the gap between users and clinicians to support more informed decision-making processes during consultations by providing key information about the progression of the skin, it's patterns and intelligent insights in between appointments. This reduces the need to rely on memory and provides a stepping stone for more constructive conversations.

A multitude of features are hosted within the app, identified by both users and clinicians as being crucial to providing remote support. derme explores areas currently untapped within the realms of digital dermatology.

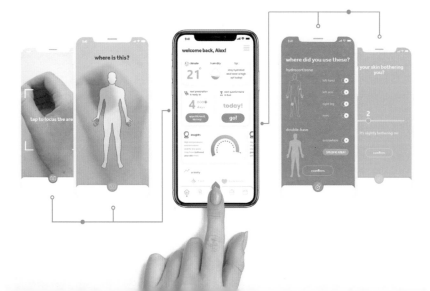

Owen Purvis
Product Design BSc

HydroSense

HydroSense is an eight-week programme that workshops a product-service system with ward-based nurses, helping them to develop healthy personal hydration behaviours and tackling the nurse dehydration problem.

During the programme, nurses form healthy hydration habits and routines using the provided technologies. Participating nurses will be given a smart fob-watch, and have a device attached to their water bottles. When shifts begin, the fob-watch starts timing the period between drinks. The three LEDs adjacent to the watch display light up incrementally with each hour that passes and begin to flash when four hours have passed. If a nurse drinks from their bottle, the 'bottle device' will communicate this to the watch. Alternatively, nurses can register drinks with a press of the 'tracker button'. Either of these actions will reset the timer and LEDs. This visualises nurses' hydration, prompting them to drink water regularly. Anonymous data collection enables iterative development of the programme, and further contributes to the research base surrounding hydration and cognition in high-pressure environments.

A collaborative project with Guy's and St Thomas' NHS Foundaton Trust

Isaac Reeves
Product Design BSc

Celli

Democratising access to a musical education - a one-size-fits-all student cello for a fraction of the cost of a traditional instrument.

It's widely accepted that learning a musical instrument as a child has a diverse range of benefits. However, all too often it is a privilege only available to those who can afford it. Celli aims to change this. Consideration of modern materials and manufacturing techniques from the beginning of the design process allows drastic cost reductions while maintaining sound quality. It also allows Celli to be adjustable, and to grow with a child throughout their musical education.

Combined with the improved hardiness of the instrument, these cost and flexibility benefits are ideal for beleaguered music services and provide great opportunities for inclusive group teaching. The construction of several prototypes has enabled feasibility testing of new design approaches, and thorough consultations with industry professionals ensures that Celli addresses the needs of both students and educators while preserving the cello's voice and soul.

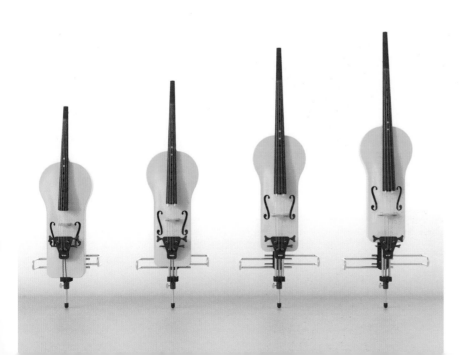

Natalia Rehakova
Industrial Design and Technology BA

Wildbyte

By tackling food waste at its source, Wildbyte provides a convenient way for millennials to access fresh local produce through a new pre-plant and pre-order system, straight from growers.

Food waste is a far-reaching problem, with large socio-economic and environmental implications. With the EU producing double their requirements, a third of UK harvests are discarded before leaving farm gates.

Wildbyte aims to address waste by highlighting the need for behavioural change and integrate the demands of emerging trends such as food transparency, convenience, and the need for ethically sourced produce. Customers pre-pay and pre-order produce directly from selected farmers for the upcoming season. This provides stability, enabling farmers to plan ahead minimising overproduction, waste, and resources significantly. By incorporating logistics and a shared economy approach, parcels can be distributed efficiently, economically, and sustainably.

Comprehending customer needs are crucial, accomplished through dietary and subscription plan analysis. Features including the virtual farmers market, food certification lab, crop-growth visualisation and sharing platform is integrated to reciprocate customer appreciation for locally grown produce.

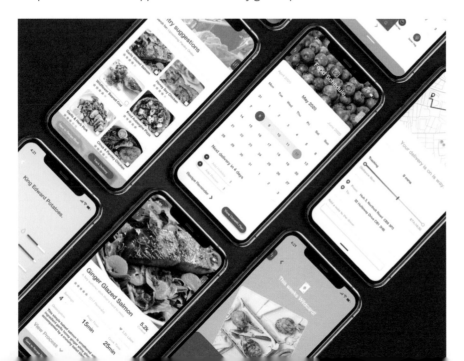

Conor Richey
Industrial Design and Technology BA

Award Winner
Best of Commercial

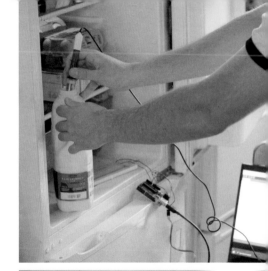

Moo. Smart Cap

A smart milk cap which can accurately predict the spoilage date of fresh milk, thus reducing milk waste in the home.

Milk waste is a huge issue currently facing the UK, with roughly 330,000 tonnes of milk being wasted annually. This issue is particularly apparent in the home, where 87% of all milk waste occurs.

The Moo. Smart Cap enables everyday milk drinkers to monitor the spoilage date of their skimmed, semi skimmed and full fat fresh milk through various internal sensors. By sampling the user's milk for factors which indicate deterioration, such as a lowering pH level or high external temperatures, the cap can determine the spoilage date of the milk. This allows the user to consume all their milk before it spoils, significantly reducing the amount of wastage.

Life cycle analysis data suggests that if implemented correctly, the Moo. Smart Cap can reduce a user's CO_2 emissions by 59kg over the product's lifespan.

Isidora Rivera Vollmer
Industrial Design and Technology BA

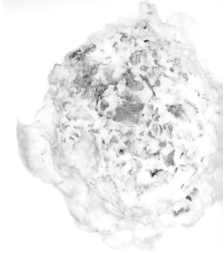

DUOS

Duos aims to create sustainable sound absorbing panels made of waste and natural materials to absorb sound within music recording and rehearsal rooms in both external institutions and at domestic enviornments.

Our planet is suffering under the consequences of unsustainable production. Many materials used in industry are exploiting the earth's resources, polluting the environment, using a lot of energy or releasing greenhouse emissions during their product life cycle. Current unsustainable sound insulation products are made of, for example, PU foam which will become an increasing environmental problem.

The opportunity arises to create modular panels made of a local, sustainable and compostable sound absorbing material with a small environmental footprint. The material is made of mainly mycelium and carrot peeling waste to absorb sound within music recording and rehearsal rooms. Circular economy models like this encourage inward investment, drive innovation, protect natural capital as well as minimise the environmental impacts of production, use and disposal.

Dante Roberts
Product Design BSc

Decrastinate

Helping university students with Attention-Deficit Hyperactivity Disorder (ADHD) achieve higher levels of focus during their independent study by implementing meditation into their study regime.

The problem of being unable to focus while studying is one shared by millions of students globally, and ADHD students find focusing much more difficult because they are easily distracted by things going on around them. Universities do offer support to these students, but as ADHD is labelled as a specific learning disability (SpLD), they only offer the same support as that offered to students with Dyslexia. ADHD is a diagnosable mental health condition which affects all aspects of a person's life, not just their learning, so in most cases students require more support than what is offered.

By using an app which encourages meditation before studying and uses webcam-based eye tracking to measure a user's focus, students can begin to become more productive as their levels of sustained concentration increase.

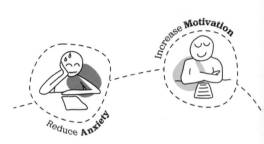

Choose a Session.

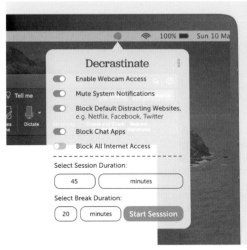

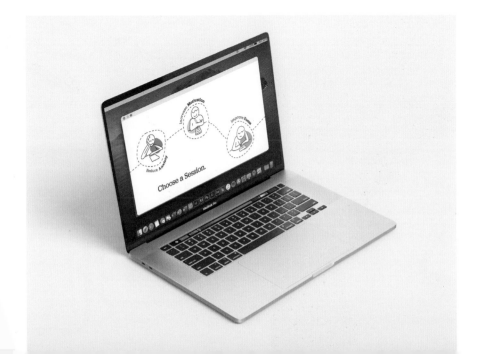

Lauren Jane Rushen
Industrial Design and Technology BA

YAC

An app produced in collaboration with Hillingdon Carers to help to provide a more efficient, digitalised service to the young adult carers they support.

The service encompasses booking of respite activities, support, learning opportunities and memories. A network is created between carers, charity, family, friends, schools and employers to support people through the key transition period that occurs between the ages of 16 and 24.

YAC encourages the public to learn about young adult carers and the issues they may face, allowing a basic access level for friends, schools and family members to access resources and converse with the staff at Hillingdon Carers. It creates a 24/7 support system by providing access to signposting materials out of normal office hours. YAC provides a comprehensive booking system to replace paper materials, allowing headcounts and medical requirements to be tracked while syncing with parents of minors allows easy collection of consent for activities. Finally, YAC provides details of learning and enrichment opportunities to expand future prospects.

A collaborative project with Hillingdon Carers

Omar Rushton
Industrial Design and Technology BA

Blob

A fitness companion that reminds and encourages physically inactive, time-starved young adults, to include and prioritise regular exercise in their day.

Over 50% of young adults aged 20-30 are not exercising to the recommended guidelines. Their busy schedule often leads to them not prioritising their health and fitness, which may increase the risk of developing physical and mental illnesses.

Blob is a physical reminder in the home with a friendly and inviting presence that works around your schedule to make exercising more approachable and achievable. Blob uses visual prompts - a red warning light to indicate when it is time to exercise, and a green light is displayed when the user has reached their fitness goals and are on track to meet the recommended guidelines.

Blob is connected via bluetooth to the Blob app, which tracks the user's progress, provides workouts and presents achievements, providing the right encouragement and facilitating appropriate workouts to ensure the user commits and engages with regular exercise.

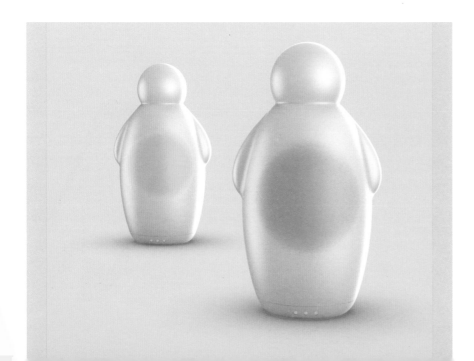

Amber Sayers
Industrial Design and Technology BA

veda

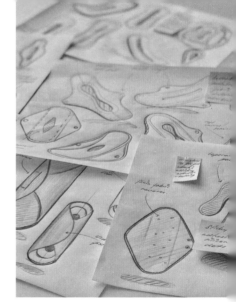

A smart and reusable pregnancy range that enables the remote monitoring of intimate health and helps to reduce the impacts of urinary and vaginal infections during pregnancy.

Urinary tract infections (UTIs) are one of the most common infections during pregnancy and are the leading cause of obstetrical ward admissions. They can lead to serious complications like premature birth and perinatal death. Whilst antibiotics are the standard treatment, overuse can contribute to antimicrobial resistance and affect foetal development. Preventative techniques are the best option to reduce incidences of UTIs and to avoid antibiotics in pregnancy.

Using a natural, holistic approach, veda can bring reassurance and empower women to take control of their intimate health during pregnancy. veda uses a colour indicating material embedded into discreet pH inserts. By identifying potentially harmful environments through a colour change, veda tracks vaginal pH and paired with recommended hygiene techniques, assists in preventing urinary and vaginal infections. The system consists of a reusable pregnancy panty-liner, pH colour inserts and an assistive app.

A collaborative project with Starling Medical Innovations

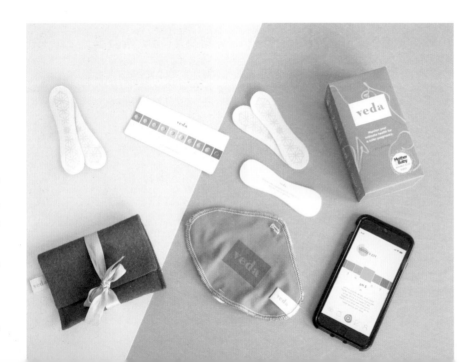

Max Schöpp
Industrial Design and Technology BA

CM via Meal Prep

Designing a financially sustainable service to treat cocaine addiction with contingency management therapy in England, via a meal preparation business.

Contingency management (CM) is a highly effective therapy for treating substance addiction; patients are incrementally rewarded for each week they are abstinent. The difficulty in implementing CM lies in the service paying its users as part of the therapy. At present the financial resources that substance addiction services have available from the NHS are limited. As such, to treat the population of 170,000 regular users of cocaine this new therapy needs to exist outside of regular funding channels. This service design consists of two halves; a meal preparation business selling meals to the public to generate revenue, and the CMT service for cocaine addicts seeking treatment. The weekly rewards are provided to service users by having their meals prepared each week they test negative. This provides effective treatment for cocaine addiction as well as the lifestyle benefits of a meal preparation service.

A collaborative project with RNS Meals

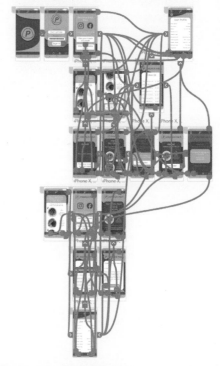

Kevin Shaji
Industrial Design and Technology BA

The Drivers Club

The Drivers Club is a new type of recovery tool aimed at creating new social interactions between male cancer patients.

Cancer is one of the most difficult life circumstances an individual can go through. During this intense period, an individual succumbs to a great deal of both physical and mental strain which includes a great sense of loneliness. Studies reveal that a patient's level of social integration and support can affect recovery rates by up to 66%.

The Drivers Club is a recovery construction kit that aims to tackle loneliness by creating an environment where patients can form friendships and become better socially-integrated into a community through competitive activity. The kit includes all the components required to form a custom Remote Control car with interchangeable cardboard bodies, which can be built and raced alongside others. This breaks the ice and allows patients to develop their social support networks amongst others in similar situations.

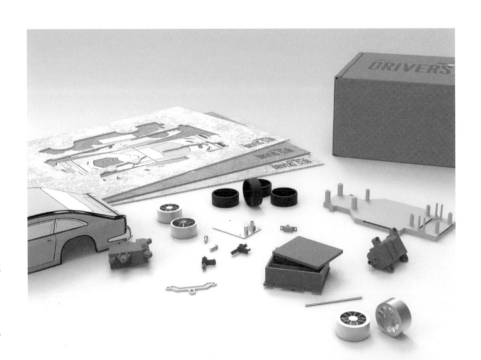

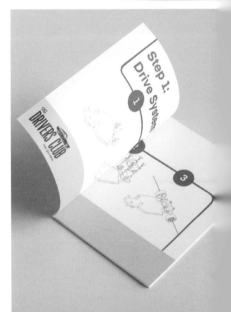

Ruoyu Shi
Product Design BSc

Wombat

Wombat aids the visually impaired to escape fires alone. Self-help and professional guidance allow the user to find both emergency first aid and the best escape path.

As the social environment develops, helping people with disabilities has received increased global attention. The purpose of this project is to help visually impaired persons living in high-rise buildings to escape fire catastrophes quickly while avoiding secondary injuries.

Wombat helps the visually impaired escape fires safely through emergency first aid, braille guidance, professional guidance and the best escape path. Design opportunities for the concept were identified through interviews with blind and relevant stakeholders, market analysis, target demographic data and user research. Functional electronic systems (GPS) and high-fidelity interactive presentations were also realised. By using the collected information, an iterative design process from sketching to CAD model creation was performed to finalise the design direction. The aesthetic design language, function and human factors were all adequately considered.

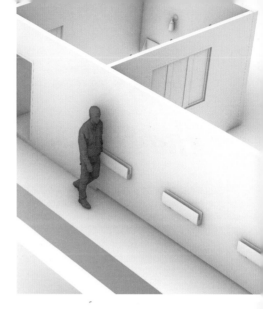

Plan the fastest escape route

Luke Smith
Product Design BSc

FIBRE

Repurposing Carbon Fibre waste to tackle aviation's hidden polluter with innovative commercially viable airline meal packaging and pre-booking service.

Aviation's contribution to global pollution through its emissions has led to increasing criticism. People, however, are less aware that catering is the industry's hidden polluter, particularly through its high content of plastic and aluminium packaging. Regulations require food and packaging waste from most international flights to be incinerated. Alongside this, aircraft manufacturers are increasingly using Carbon Fibre as it is light-weight and strong but currently its end-of-life solutions are limited.

FIBRE proposes an environmentally sound catering package in line with international regulations which is achieved by combining lightweight reusable recycled Carbon Fibre dishes with compostable packaging and an online meal pre-booking service. The design could reduce meal weight by 86% per passenger and carbon output by 581kg/CO2 per 1000 meals when analysed against recent industry statistics. This translates to potential annual savings of £7.1-53 million for airlines.

Harry Snow
Product Design Engineering BSc

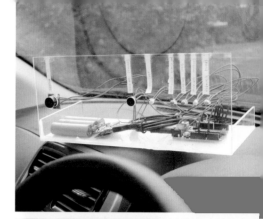

Introl

Introl is a warning system to prevent distraction and improve awareness whilst in control of a vehicle, by monitoring the driver, the road and the cars nearby.

With total driven miles increasing to a record high in 2018 and Driver Error based incidents remaining a majority, there is a significant problem that Introl can have a credible impact.

Introl will combine driver-state assessment technology to determine the driver's level of attention to the road, minimising driver error and environment assessment to give the driver a better sense of the area surrounding the car.

This system will include a CPU that can collect and process data from all other modules via Bluetooth, powered by the 9V outlet, a blind-spot sensor that looks behind and warns the driver of an approaching vehicle, a parking sensor that can look for close objects and warn the driver of any nearby obstacles, and a driver monitoring sensor to make sure that they are paying attention by tracking their eyes.

Luke Tolchard
Industrial Design and Technology BA

Polar Dynamics

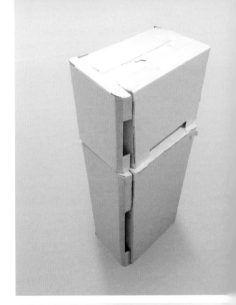

Redesigning a manufacturing solution to produce prosthetics for lower limb amputees with significant improvements to product performance and reduction in production time.

Prosthetics for Lower Limb Amputees (LLA) have been neglected regarding their material and function performance. Current manufacturing techniques are limiting the progression of these products and, therefore, leading to lower-performance components. The use of Liquid Additive Manufacturing along with Polar Architecture produces products with significant benefits to product longevity, performance and reduction in manufacturing time.

The final deliverable is a solution for the 3D manufacturing of lower limb prosthetic sockets for a lower cost, with a massive reduction in time, and significantly greater customisability with a greater degree of finetuning. This leads to a prosthetic socket for a lower limb amputee that is functional and stable enough to compete with current market sockets, offering a new solution to a stagnant market.

A collaborative project with DSM / Blatchford / KMWE

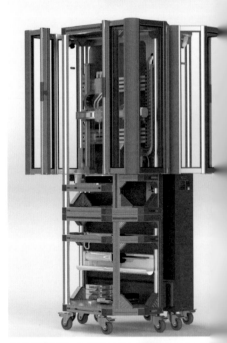

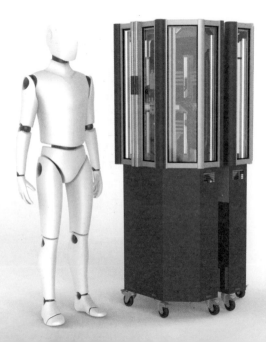

Naomi Tucker
Product Design BSc

Shiloh

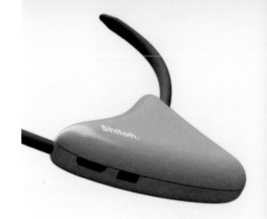

A monitoring and alarm device for patients with high cardiovascular risk, with a mobile app which will help promote healthy behaviours.

Cardiovascular disease (CVD) refers to a group of conditions which affect the heart and blood vessels, causing heart attacks and strokes. It is the number 1 cause of death globally, causing around 31% of deaths. The risk factors are; smoking, lack of exercise, diet, obesity, age, family history and hypertension, with hypertension being a cause in half of strokes and heart attacks in the UK.

This project aims to create a device that acts as an alarm system in the event of a stroke or heart attack and empower the user to make changes and reduce their risk of progression of the disease. The outcome is a device that monitors heart rate, blood pressure and core body temperature, with a mobile app which will educate the user, allowing them to be more proactive in managing their condition.

A collaborative project with The Imagination Factory

Daniel Valentine
Industrial Design and Technology BA

Alorem

Making allergy immunotherapy treatment as easy as brushing your teeth, so helping patients to fully complete their treatment and achieve a better quality of life.

The Alorem toothbrush doses allergy therapy while the patient brushes their teeth. The therapy is a personalised allergen formulation, slowly desensitising the patient's immune system from reacting to the allergy in the future, a treatment known as allergy immunotherapy.

The allergy immunotherapy is contained within the toothbrush head and is dispensed by a diaphragm pump connected to a piezoelectric driver accurately controlling the release of the therapy. The pump is actuated by an accelerometer and infra-red sensors, so delivering doses at effective locations within the mouth.

Aligning the treatment to brushing teeth helps to make the task habitual, therefore helping to maintain long term adherence which is needed for long term effectiveness of allergy immunotherapy. The brush collects data from each brushing session to ensure that treatment is being administered correctly, with problems areas highlighted within the app.

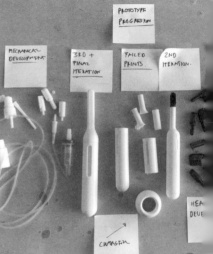

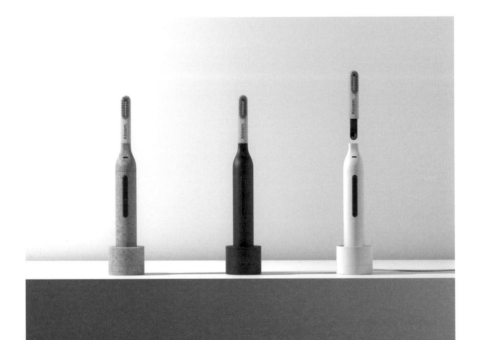

Charlie Wilson
Industrial Design and Technology BA

LumoFuel Bioreactor

LumoFuel is a domestic bioreactor that cultivates algae and processes it into low emission, carbon neutral biodiesel that can be used to run an unaltered diesel engine.

Transportation accounts for around 30% of global greenhouse gas emissions, with personal transport making up a large part of the average driver's personal carbon footprint.

As algae grows it absorbs light and CO_2 from the atmosphere, producing purified oxygen and energy, stored in the forms of energy dense oils called lipids. Nannochloropsis Oculata is the species used in the bioreactor for it's high lipid content and ability to double its colony size in 24 hours under ideal conditions. Once the colony is mature, the product automatically drains half of each grow tube, extracting the algal lipids and processing them into around three litres of biodiesel per day. Drawing power from a 1kW solar module, LumoFuel produces biodiesel that is net carbon neutral, with any CO_2 released during combustion having been originally absorbed by the algae during photosynthesis.

Ben Younger
Industrial Design and Technology BA

Scopum

Enhancing the potential and usability of consumer UVB phototherapy products for Psoriasis treatment by combining emerging LED technology and user-centric product design.

Skin cells are commonly made and replaced every 3-4 weeks, but with Psoriasis this process only takes 3-7 days, resulting in red outbreaks across the body. Phototherapy is a highly successful treatment of Psoriasis as UV light penetrates the skin and has the ability to re-regulate the skin's life-cycle. However, existing consumer products provide an unnecessarily high exposure to UV, are not adaptable and are mains-powered.

Scopum (derived from the Latin word for target) offers corrections to existing flawed designs, with an interchangeable product mask for different sized patches allowing a more targeted treatment to an isolated outbreak. In addition, the design has a rechargeable internal battery which was made possible by using UV LEDs as opposed to large light fixtures. Therefore, Scopum empowers its users to complete their skin treatment wherever they feel comfortable.

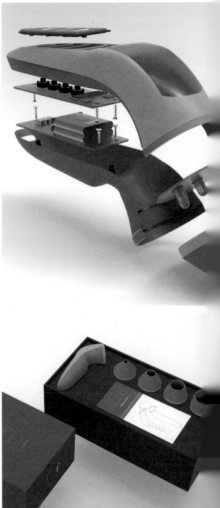

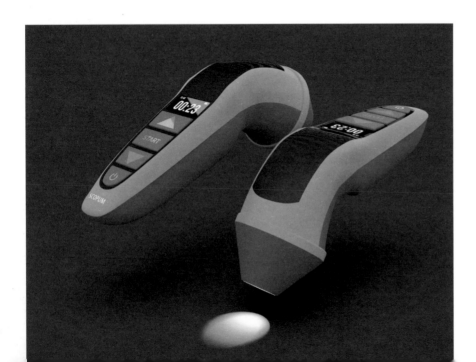

Minnan Yu
Product Design Engineering BSc

OSC

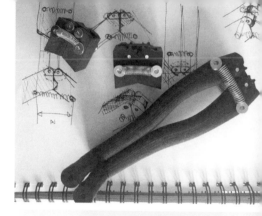

The Ozonated Showering Console (OSC) uses the Ozonated Showering Technology to prevent and treat pressure ulcers and related dermatological disorders.

Ozonated Showering Technology (OST), a groundbreaking way to treat and prevent pressure ulcers and related dermatological disorders, was recently invented by Huaxin Yu and the Southern Medical University of China.

Inspired by OST, this version of the Ozonated Showering Console (along with a tailored business model, Ozonated Showering Service (OSS)), aims to take OST to a broader population in the UK, tackling one of the major medical issues for the elderly generation and the diabetic population. By focusing on the direct prevention of the initial formation of pressure ulcers rather than treatment or detection at a later stage, OSS breaks the negative cycle of ulcer formation and may save a substantial amount of resources both at a public and individual level.

A collaborative project with Huaxin Yu and Southern Medical University of China

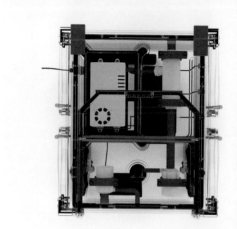

CONTE
DESIG

Marjan Angoshtari
Lecturer in Industrial Design – Module Leader

The Contextual Design module is a multifaceted project that combines a well-executed design innovation process with brand-repositioning. In this module, students tackle some of the most challenging problems facing our world in the next decade. In the past three years of leading the module, I have had the privilege of working alongside a fantastic team of like-minded designers who have shared my passion for design and have continuously provided students with an excellent level of support and guidance. Clare Brass has been a true source of inspiration for the module since 2017/18; Benjamin Parton and

Sandra Fruebing worked tirelessly alongside me for many long hours throughout this academic year.

What follows is a reflection of the hard work and tireless efforts of a group of students and staff who went to great lengths to make this year's projects a reality. This includes our final year students of design, the Contextual Design teaching team and Paul Josse and his team of technicians at our design workshops.

XTUAL

WWF

The housing crisis is a large-scale issue increasingly affecting people in the UK. Young adults are most impacted with 40% not being able to afford homes. This motivates people to look to alternative solutions such as off-grid housing. In response, some organisations seek to build affordable, self-sufficient communities with net zero carbon emissions. Generally, people lack the confidence and skills to make the big change to off-grid living. Through design thinking our group aimed to provide people with this confidence.

1. *Somm* | Amber Sayers

Organic matter is the very foundation for healthy and productive soils and is vital for sustainable farming in the future. Somm encourages a soil centric, conservational farming approach for off-grid communities by monitoring soil organic matter and carbon storage.

2. *Ping* | Arthur Brooks

Ping connects you with every member of your new community, giving you as well as everyone else the opportunity to share skills and knowledge, leading to a welcoming, friendly community.

3. *Flux* | Katie Price

When faced with limited, seasonal ingredients in off-grid communities, healthy and exciting dishes can always be created by utilising aroma analysis technology to match complimentary ingredients. Flux helps to create ideal food combinations and confidence in home cooking.

4. *Shift* | Luke Smith

Shift enables the free-flow of electricity within an off-grid community, using wireless energy transfer and micro-grid infrastructure. Communities will be able to share electricity with neighbours and manage energy in situations where this currently is not possible.

5. *Loop* | Oliver Martin

Biodiversity is essential to creating rich and productive ecosystems. Loop allows you to connect with birds in your garden through a unique and immersive experience, interpreting bird songs and alarms, enabling you to accommodate to their specific needs and requirements.

Award Winner
Best Contextual
Design Project

DK

As we are living longer, the differences in opinions and beliefs between our generations are becoming more pronounced. Innovation and technological development haven't tended to particularly account for the older generations, leading to a technological divide between old and young. Communication between generations has consequently become harder, as each generation gets set in their ways. This division between generations is commonly known as the "Generation Gap."

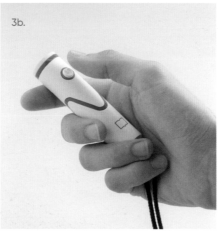

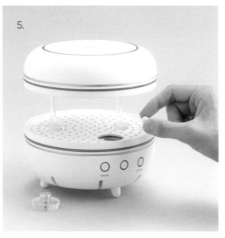

1. *Epoch* | Andrew Pickering

Using a unique, family-centred social platform, Epoch gently notifies you when a memento of a predecessor is close by. Open the flexible, roll up screen to inspect the object and discover the ancestral memory associated with it.

2. *Hot Potato* | Arphatsara Paowana

DK Hot Potato is a device encouraging detached family members to have a more satisfying conversation and a deeper connection with their family in a family gathering when time is limited, involving everyone to share their stories and experiences.

3. *Distance* | Conor Richey

DK Distance focuses on reconnecting grandparents and grandchildren separated by long-distances through sharing cuisine. By sharing classic family recipes, as well as newly discovered recipes from across the globe, DK Distance builds upon shared experiences to reconnect loved ones.

4. *Link* | Matt Gardner

The always-on aspect of modern technology prevents students from finding opportunities to reach out to their grandparents. DK Link breaks through the din and acts as a stimulus for communication by using electrodes to trigger neural pathways which spark the desire.

5. *Discussion* | Shivy Das

Students' interests are used to create connections to curriculum topics which teachers use as discussion points, opening up dialogue between two generations. The device creates a tactile holographic mind map of the discourse for a memorable active learning experience.

JCB

According to the Environment Agency, 1 in 6 properties in the UK are at risk of flooding, with the frequency of river flooding predicted to double or even quadruple by 2080. Currently 5 million people are at risk of displacement from floods, and they costs the UK government £1.4 billon a year. How can we reposition JCB as a British brand that cares for the growing natural disaster that is flooding in the UK?

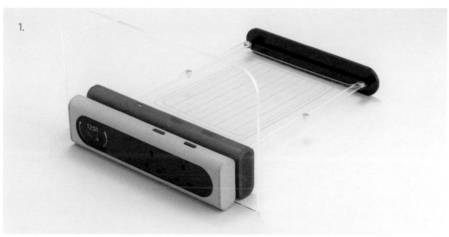

1. *Power Generator* | Amin Haruna

The JCB Power Generator is a backup power supply that generates and stores electricity to ensure that flood victims have access to a safe and reliable power supply during a flood-induced power outage.

2. *Poseidon* | Kevin Shaji

The Poseidon is an aqua drone that helps users navigate safely through floodwater using an array of sonar and lidar sensors to map out the flood floor and subsequently optimal safe travel routes.

3. *Guardian* | Sirtaj Singh Ghata-Aura

Guardian is an automated fire prevention system to help protect homes after the event of a flood, from the risks of electric fires. Integrated infrared cameras use radio waves to detect fires and extinguish them before serious damage is caused.

4. *Manta* | Seb Parker

Manta is an autonomous vehicle which uses an amphibious undulating fin design to act as a compact, foldable platform for road users, allowing them to remotely assess flood depth and flow on roads before crossing, and to alert other drivers.

5. *Home Defence System* | Thomas Knipe

A smart augmented reality device that will alert you on flood warnings, scan your home's infrastructure for weaknesses or cracks and advise how to fix them, and calm you down in a panic situation by analysing your body language.

Muji

Over time Muji's products have become a unique approach to minimalism, providing vital functions and excluding non-essential elements, reflecting their catchphrase "Lower priced for a reason". So how can Muji help those on a low income have a brighter and warmer life in a future of ever-increasing energy costs? Taking on Muji's values, our team has developed products and services that aim to improve everyday life for people in low income fuel poverty.

1.

2a.

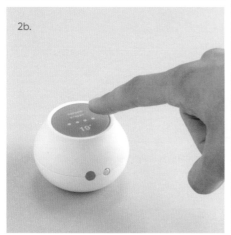

2b.

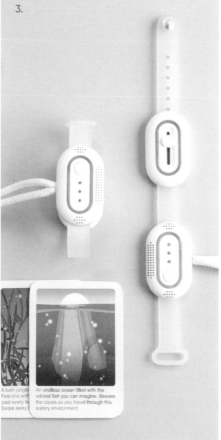

1. *Sōji* | Natalia Rehakova

Sōji is a convenient handheld cleaning device which prides itself in significantly reducing utility costs by providing an efficient targeted solution for garments using the power of CO_2, paired with automated ETag scanning abilities to gauge optimal cycle settings.

2. *Oto* | Omar Rushton

A piezoelectric device placed in noise polluted cities that harvests sound energy to be converted to electricity for fuel-poor elderly. The user-friendly control device allows the resident to activate their daily hour of free electricity and monitor their usage and room temperature.

3. *Tanoshi* | Justine Raven Fernandez

A games console stripped down to its fundamental core – imagination. With no screen, cards are used to prompt children's creative imagination. Haptic feedback through ultrasound speakers allow exploration through different environments while the fast-paced motions involved charge the highly efficient device.

Kinder

Education is the foundation of a child's life, and schools are fundamental for children to develop cognitive skills and social relationships. As the population continues to rise the number of disengaged children in education is becoming a major issue. This is why we believe that repositioning Kinder to target the education system would be beneficial for the future of education. Our aim is to provide these marginalised children with the tools to succeed by encouraging an integrative approach to learning.

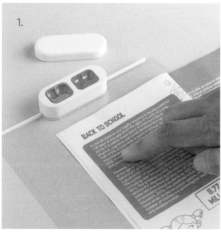

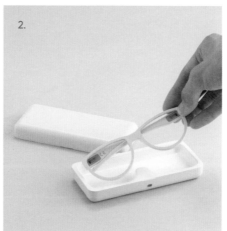

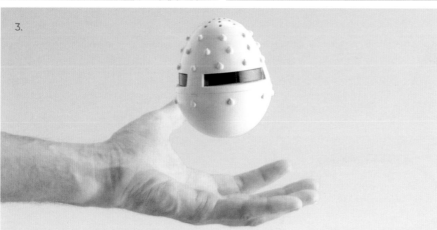

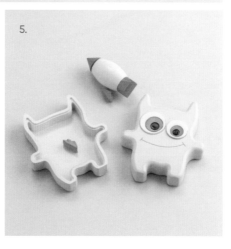

1. *View* | Victoria Poizer

Kinder View will encourage children with dyslexia to excel and feel integrated in mainstream education. The device is aimed to reduce the phonological challenges that many dyslexic children face when reading, allowing the child to maintain independence in the classroom.

2. *Empathy* | Chi Wong

A product that can be implemented in your school which provides the ability for teachers to visualise their students emotional state, thus allowing the teacher to deliver their classes more effectively and creating an environment better catered to all students.

3. *Shake* | Chris Delaney

Kinder Shake, aimed at bilingual students in primary schools, employs the gamification of cultural and lingual learning through a voice controlled smart 'egg' that offers real time translation and feedback through AI.

4. *Raum* | Aman Coutts

Redefining the playground to become more inclusive for the greater primary student population and to minimise the use of technological devices during break times in order to stimulate the brain in more effective ways.

5. *Achieve* | Megan King

Kinder Achieve is a learning tool that engages disadvantaged pupils with their learning, through earning small incentives that create memorable moments of surprise, which have a lasting impact on the child's attitude to education allowing them to achieve their potential.

Kodak

It is not always possible for families to spend time together, so it is of huge importance that the time they do spend together is treasured and enjoyed. Kodak hopes to not only capture special family moments, but help create new moments of joy through design solutions suitable for the families of the future. These solutions help families make the most of time spent together and feel more connected when they are apart.

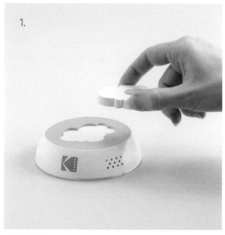

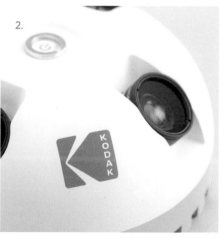

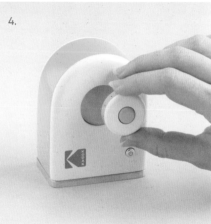

1. *Stories* | Caitlin Beer

Kodak Stories aims to create more special moments between a father and child when they cannot be together. Using developing dream technology, the device influences dreams through the use of sounds, bringing bedtime stories to life.

2. *Community* | Jack Day

This product aims to reduce anxiety in long-term paediatric patients and help combat their inherent loneliness. The mood sensor recognises anxiety, prompting the projector to turn the cubical into a 4D natural environment, where they can digitally meet likeminded children.

3. *Kinnect* | Luke Tolchard

Kodak Kinnect has been developed to seamlessly integrate into the home. Using existing military communication methods as a guideline, Kinnect can transform any audio or message-based communication system into a 3D projection of that individual talking and interacting with you.

4. *Breathe* | Hannah Coombs

Kodak Breathe is a wearable device and home hub set for working mothers, that captures memorable moments through aroma. These aromas are released to remind mothers of positive experiences with her child whilst apart, and encourage self-care practices.

5. *Share* | Ruby Ovenden

The Kodak Share is an accessory designed to aid carers and social workers in their efforts to rehabilitate children within the foster care system. It will do so by monitoring their emotions through expression recognition and pulse reading.

Channel 4

With global poverty rates set to rise with population growth over the next 10-15 years, the poorest in society, particularly those in cities, are set to be disproportionately effected, making basic essentials such as quality nutrition, shelter, clean water and affordable energy less attainable. How can Channel 4, through smarter design thinking help to provide the poorest in society with these basic essentials?

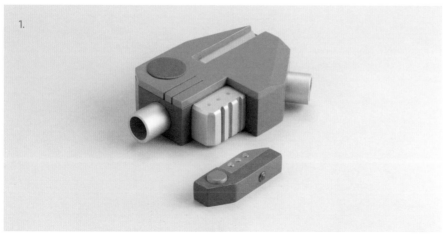

1.

2.

3.

1. *Hydro-Clo* | Tanaka Bofu

Hydro-Clo looks into the next 20-30 years to reinvent the application of plumbing in new build council homes, providing Hydroelectricity using the in flowing water of the home, to provide low cost sustainable energy.

2. *Talia* | Naomi Tucker

Talia aims to tackle reduced rates of breastfeeding by using volumetric imaging to project women breastfeeding in public spaces around the city, increasing awarness and access to reliable information on the subject.

3. *Arda* | Charlie Wilson

ARDA utilises hot composting of organic household waste to produce temperatures of up to 75°C which are circulated around it's radiator, heating the users home, without adding to their bills.

Land Rover

The supply of affordable housing in the UK is not keeping up with demand and with a projected house price rise of 140% in the next 10 years, more and more people are looking for novel and sustainable ways to live.

There has been a 246% increase of people living on our waterways since 2012. With this uptake of water-based living expected to continue, more people are in need of support to face the challenges of house boating.

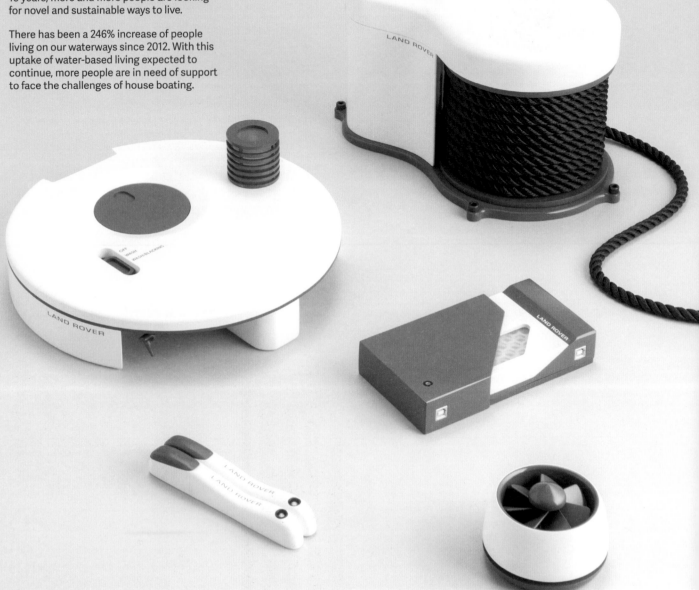

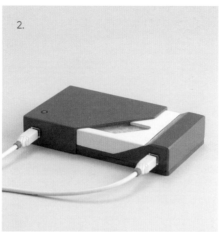

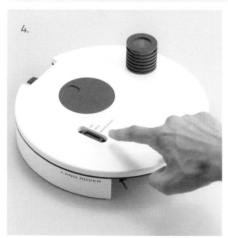

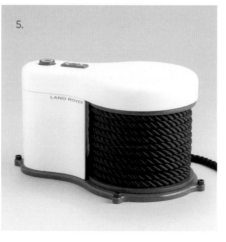

1. *Flight* | Toby Middleton

Summoned via a smartphone app, this drone's main purpose it to guide users along the towpath at night, lighting the path in front and recording the journey through a small camera lens.

2. *Pulse* | Max Mitchell

Pulse utilises end-of-life lithium-ion batteries from electric powered cars to power narrowboats. Based on a Tesla Model S, used batteries are split into 16 modules which can be placed around the boat to maintain ballast.

3. *Scout* | Harry Cozens

The Learning Assistant Scout is designed for children on British canals, providing them with lessons that are inspired by their natural environment and geographical location, aiding their education while their home is on the move.

4. *Skate* | Toby Allen

Skate is a hassle free hull service from JLR. Using electro magnets Skate temporarily adheres itself to the boat's exterior and uses canal water jets to clean the hull, before respraying the boat with hull blacking.

5. *Hitch* | Edmund Miles

Hitch makes navigating a canal lock safer and easier. It automatically adjusts the length of the centre rope as the water level changes, holding the narrowboat in the correct location within the lock and reducing the risk of sinking.

Life | Mia Alamo

Land Rover Life restores the magic in living amongst nature's medicine. Life allows users to identify, forage and use the nature that is on your doorstep for medical purposes. This creates a more unique and easy approach to healthcare. (not pictured)

Oatly

The earth is getting hotter. Average global temperature is set to rise by around 1.5°C by 2030. In the summer of 2018, 863 deaths in the over-65's were heat-related. It is estimated that, over the next 10-15 years, an extreme heatwave is likely to occur every other year. As the UK is already coping with an aging population, there will be an increasing number of people at risk, creating opportunities to tackle emerging issues in new ways.

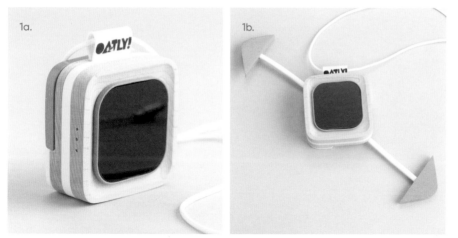

1a.

1b.

2.

3.

1. *SOS Assistant* | Isidora Rivera Vollmer

Heatwaves have been associated with a 14% increase in the risk of out-of-hospital cardiac arrests (OHCA). The SOS Assistant revolutionises the way to restore a normal heart rhythm during heat-related OHCAs involving older adults in 10-15 years' time.

2. *Adaptive Jacket* | Pashywn Cabral

A jacket that blocks UV radiation and keeps a stable body temperature during heatwaves. This concept jacket features a variety of smart materials, such as photochromic material located on highly exposed areas that reflect harsh UV rays.

3. *Window-Blind* | Lihao Chen

Window-Blind helps elderly people regulate their temperature and reduce the risk of cardiovascular disease. An evaporative cooling system, it uses metal-organic framework to condense water molecules from air passing through a window, cooling it and reducing room temperature.

PG Tips

By 2041, the homeless population is predicted to double. In England alone, there are an estimated 277,000 people considered to be homeless, 33,000 of whom are young, first-time homeless aged 16-24, many forced to leave their homes through no fault of their own. This age group is also where an intervention could have the greatest impact. PG Tips aims to provide a helping hand for the young homeless, by increasing stability and promoting a sense of purpose.

1.

2.

3.

4.

5.

1. *Ring* | Charlie Boyle

Ring is designed to support the homeless youth by simplifying the process of reporting hate crimes, reducing anxiety and leading victims to safer areas. Over time the data can be used to build a network of 'verified' safe areas and services.

2. *City Share* | Lewis Muggeridge

City Share is a product/service that provides the homeless population access to unused showers, toilets and laundrettes in the city. The device can be mounted on ground floor office windows for easy access.

3. *Roam* | Harry Snow

With an ever increasing need for social interaction and connections, Roam connects the young homeless with animal owners through their shared love of animals, bringing together communities and like minded people.

4. *Ethos* | Charlie Gilks

A tool that helps a young homeless person's re-development of the soft skills lost in a period of homelessness through holographic communication with their new employer. Each keeps one half, and records messages for the other outside of the workplace.

5. *Portal* | Stuart Meredith

A device to help build and maintain the bond between young mothers and children who have been separated due to homelessness. Portal records bedtime stories from the mother which the child can then view and interact with.

Ben & Jerry's

85% of parents in the UK do not let their children play freely outdoors due to fears for their children's safety and security. Today, only 21% of children regularly play outside compared to 71% of their parents' generation. This is worse for children in cities, and with a further 10% of the population living in cities by 2030 this situation will only be exacerbated. Allowing children to play unaccompanied during childhood improves personal, social and emotional development.

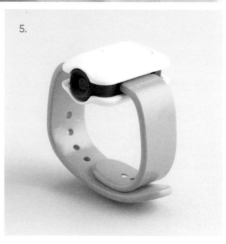

1. *Sense* | Caitlyn Morton

Taken from the concept of 'spider sense' being able to sense danger before it happens. This device will allow the wearer to 'sense' when a dangerous situation is arising by sounding an alarm, allowing the wearer to react.

2. *Anonomeyes* | Lauren Rushen

A response to the rising rates of knife crime in London, Anonomeyes is a wearable device that provides an anonymous way for young people to report crime and serious violence, creating an intelligent network where peers can learn from one another.

3. *Scanability* | Helen Bellhouse

A hand held device to aid decision making when independently choosing what to eat by changing a child's motivations. Scanability scans a child's plate and encourages them to eat healthier based on achieving badges pre set by the parent.

4. *FreeFrame* | Max Schöpp

FreeFrame is a canvas that can create art on any surface, enabling children to explore their creativity. Countering the lack of funding for art and design in schools and providing security in the development of skills essential for personal growth.

5. *Palmap* | Samuel Bušovský

A wearable device to aid children navigate their environments independently without the need for a distracting mobile device. Palmap projects intuitive directions onto the user's palm guiding them to a pre-set home destination which is updated in real time.

Pixar

Attention deficit hyperactivity disorder (ADHD) is a neurodevelopment disorder which is one of the most common mental health conditions affecting children and adults. ADHD is a global condition impacting 130 million 5-19 year-olds, not including those undiagnosed. Pixar distinguishes itself through inclusivity in film, to socially engineer new perspectives and educate on an emotional level. We have repositioned Pixar as a brand for parents of, and children with ADHD to create interventions that redefine their stories.

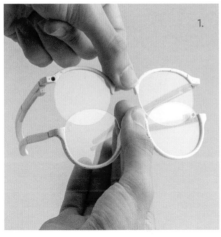

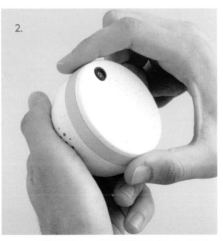

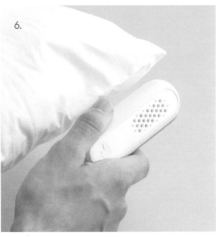

1. *Memo* | Elise Filleul

Augmented reality glasses which can be split into two to assist a child with ADHD. Together it helps them maintain their focus, and when split it allows the child to let someone into their internal world to build stronger bonds.

2. *Temu* | Oliver Lambert

Redefining time awareness for children with ADHD. Distractibility and hyper-focus are common attributes of ADHD that distorts a child's sense of time. Temu is an active timer that converts routine into music and visuals that help children stay focused.

3. *Empa* | Tanaka Kungwengwe

An assistant for ADHD children that provides them with a visual emotional language to interpret the emotions of others during everyday social interactions. Empa helps ADHD children to develop empathy, so that they can form and sustain interpersonal relationships.

4. *Self Reflect* | Arun Chalotra

Self Reflect is a smart mirror that uses Augmented Reality (AR) to improve the parent and ADHD child's communication through an immersive self-affirmation ritual designed for the morning routine, building the ADHD child's confidence and expression deficits.

5. *Bondi* | Daniel Valentine

Redefining bonding between parents and ADHD children, helping children to share highs and lows from their day to ensure that children communicate well to their parents to help build a stronger emotional connection.

6. *PillowAngel* | William Vickery

PillowAngel helps children fall asleep by drawing on Pixar's vast library of stories and narrates them to a child in bed at night. Using EEG and machine learning PillowAngel learns which stories are most effective at getting children to sleep.

Twinings

Single parent families account for nearly
a quarter of all households globally. This
statistic is matched within the UK and set to
rise by 22% in the next 15 years. Everyday a
single parent makes life changing decisions
and sacrifices that two parent households
simply don't have to make, due to the
responsibility of raising their child alone.

1. *Mentor* | Andrew Gardner

The Mentor makes it easier for single parents, who may have limited time, to learn something new. Through the use of 3D holograms and infrared sensors the Mentor provides an immersive learning experience.

2. *ShowMe Pods* | Ben Younger

This product empowers less technologically proficient guardians to capture precious memories of children for absent working single parents. The audio-triggered black recording pod tracks motion to capture footage, while the white pod acts as a playback projector for the parent.

3. *Head To Toe* | Stephanie Tomlinson

Head To Toe will hyper economise your household by tracking tone of voice, pulse and temperature for accurate assessment of need. The wearable sensors for the ankle and mouth adjust your home to suit your mood automatically and precisely.

4. *Balance* | Angus Galton

Balance is a mixed reality headset for non-amicable parents, that empowers co-parenting and immersive parent-child connection; Exposing the child to more beneficial scenarios and experiences that are seen in two-parent households.

5. *Drawings* | Jake O'Sullivan

A single parent is four times more likely to date another single parent than someone without a child. Drawings is the ultimate icebreaker, with dates designed to provide a platform to bring single parent families together through fun, getting-to-know-you activities.

6. *Sono Pod* | Charlotte Ansell

A digital meditation therapy pod that encourages a full 8 hours of sleep by minimising the time taken for single parents to re-enter their sleep cycle through the natural science behind aromatherapy, heat therapy and Howlite stone. This creates the ultimate meditative sleep setting.

Lush

With nomadic lifestyles on the rise, the World Bank estimates that 250 million people live outside their country of birth. As the world is becoming smaller, net migration is projected to account for the majority of population growth by 2050. With increased levels of cultural diversity, fewer people feel a sense of belonging to their community. This opens up new possibilities to reimagine how people integrate, settle and coexist in new environments.

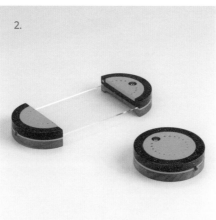

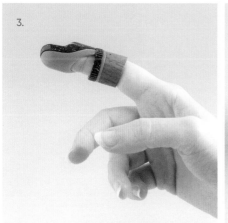

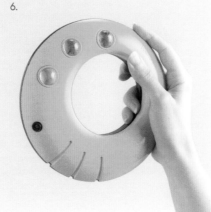

1. *Drop of Love* | Fatima Hermosin Acasuso

Stay connected with your loved ones through the distance by reliving unique and unforgettable moments experienced with them. By wearing this necklace, your best memories will be recorded and projected whenever you need them the most.

2. *Photo Bomb* | Maria Alejandra Pinilla Pease

Photo Bomb aims to redefine interpersonal communication through the shared language of pictures and sounds. Combining the use of cameras, projectors, and AI, Photo Bomb allows users to tag sounds to pictures and share their unique experiences.

3. *Listen'In* | Nivedhaa Muthu

A wearable communications device that connects travellers in a new place by initiating social engagement during their journeys. Nomads can tune into live conversations of their interests with those they usually wouldn't and forge new friendships along the way.

4. *Patch of Heaven* | Niamh Cogley-Rock

This adhesive patch replenishes, revitalises and rejuvenates nomads as they travel globally. Allowing different nutrient and vitamin bombs to be slotted in and dissolve into the body over a period of months tailored to the user's personal health.

5. *Me Myself & I* | Viraj Javaharlal

A bracelet keeping you self-aware about the changes you endure during your travels. Built to remind you who you are in this fast-paced world so you can stay true to yourself and never forget what builds your identity.

6. *Ripples n' Rays* | Yash Bhansali

Build a vibrant palette of sights and sounds from places you've experienced along your travels. Using this interactive brush set, create a sense of escape in your bedroom and transform your windows into dynamic paintings. Piece together your new home.

EMBED
SYSTE

Dr Federico Colecchia
Lecturer in Creative Electronics and Programming

Electronics are ubiquitous and an important aspect of everyday life - often an integral part of the products we use.

The main objective of the Embedded Systems for Design module is for students to gain a basic theoretical understanding and have hands-on experience with programmable 'single-chip computers' to be embedded within products, with a view to enabling specific functionalities and enhancing the user experience. Practical labs in first term pave the way to the second term project, where students get to individually design and fabricate a 'smart' product of their choosing, with custom electronics embedded in it. Each student is completely in charge of their own Embedded Systems project, providing a good opportunity for developing further project and time management skills, There is room for collaboration among students on this module too, with some of the best student submissions featuring in Made in Brunel over the years.

DED
1S

Peter Bushell
Product Design Engineering BSc

Herb Incubator

Autonomously monitor and maintain herbs or small plants in a controlled environment to maximise growth during the key early stages.

This is a prototype for an automatic herb incubator which monitors the plant's environment and actively supports its growth. The incubator measures the moisture content of the soil and the ambient light to automatically irrigate and provide artificial light when needed. Pressing the status button presents the soil moisture content and ambient light as percentages on the display.

The ambient light is measured using an LDR, the analogue voltage is mapped to a PWM signal sent to an LED strip which varies instantly and continuously with changing light conditions. All the automatic functions and monitoring are handled in an interrupt service routine using Timer_0. This allows the PIC to carry out overlapping functions, for example continuing to update the LEDs as light conditions vary while the status is being displayed on screen or the motor is running the irrigation.

Pippa Copeland
Product Design BSc

CPR Teddy Bear

The CPR Teddy Bear allows children to learn CPR techniques and rhythms without being as intimidating as a traditional CPR mannequin.

There have been several news stories of children as young as 9 saving adults' lives by administering CPR, yet more often than not children are not taught these vital skills until they are much older.

The Teddy Bear consists of a soft switch in the bears chest to simulate CPR chest compressions. This comprises two layers of conductive fabric separated between a doughnut shaped layer of foam to ensure the conductive fabrics only touched when pressed. When the chest is compressed, an interrupt registers on the PIC and the rate at which the chest is pressed is displayed on the LCD screen. When the CPR routine is correctly completed, the LED heart 'beats' through pulse width modulation.

This toy could also encourage children to pursue careers in medicine or first response.

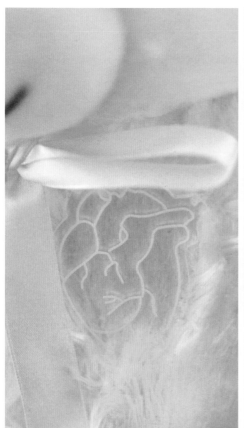

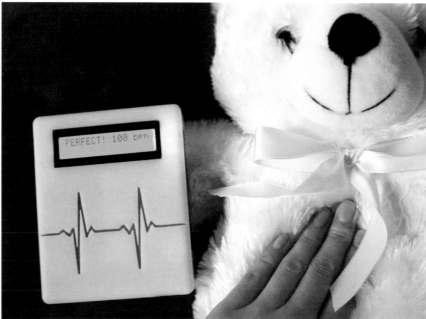

George Farren
Product Design Engineering BSc

Sun Cream Dispenser

A dispenser for public venues which dispenses portions of sun-cream. It measures the UV intensity from the sun, and warns users of high UV levels, encouraging them to get sun-cream.

A wall mounted sun cream dispenser for sunny public venues such as beaches & parks. The dispenser uses an IR sensor to detect user's hands and dispenses individual portions of sun cream, without the user requiring physical contact with the dispenser.

The dispenser uses a UV sensor to measure the intensity of the sun's UV rays, and when they reach a threshold, a warning light displays informing users the sun is very intense and that they should apply sun cream.

The sun cream cartridges are easily replaceable, with buttons to control the dispensing carriage. Internal limit switches prevent the dispenser from over dispensing when empty. The dispenser is made from an acrylic housing, with a robust linear actuator for driving the dispense mechanism. The control board is a custom milled 2-sided circuit board and utilises the PIC-16F819 microcontroller.

Evelyn Harris
Product Design BSc

Plant Grow Station

The plant growing station assists the user to grow plants more effectively, by measuring and displaying information about the plant.

The plant growing station is designed to aid the user to look after a plant by providing information about the plant's environment. Sensors on the prototype record information such as temperature and light levels. By measuring these levels, the plant growing station can turn on its LEDs when it detects the light reaching the plant is too low.

The LEDs provide the plant with white, red and blue light. Red light is essential for a plant's early life including seed germination and root growth, in addition to stimulating the growth of flowers and fruit, while blue light is known to promote chlorophyll production which helps to keep leaves and stems healthy and the strong. The plant growing station also assists the efficiency of the plant's growth by rotating the plant to ensure uniform light distribution.

Jonathan James
Product Design Engineering BSc

Desktop Climate Control

Desktop Climate Control allows office workers to customise the air temperature in their work space without disturbing other office workers.

With multiple users in an office environment, it is inevitable that the room temperature setting will not be right for everybody. To combat this, this miniature climate control unit allows individuals to both cool and warm their personal space. The system is sympathetic to a limited space work environment and allows items such as mugs and plant pots to be stored on its upper face.

The unit has a simple user interface that allows users to specify their target temperature or, using the MAX feature, have a

minute kick of warm air. Current temperatures and target temperatures are displayed through a 16x2 LCD screen which can be turned off whilst not in use.

The system is controlled by a PIC microcontroller which is programmed to control the onboard silicone heater and fan, to output air that is thermally regulated to the desired temperature.

David Paling
Product Design BSc

Self-Watering Tool

A device used in greenhouses to monitor growing conditions, to change the frequency of the watering process to provide optimum growth for plants.

By monitoring soil humidity, light intensity and temperature inside a greenhouse, the device will change how often the plants need to be watered. For example on an overcast rainy day, the plants will need to be watered less often than a bright sunny day. This is achieved using an analogue soil moisture sensor, an analogue thermometer and a light dependent resistor.

The soil moisture sensor is simply inserted into the soil where the user would like to monitor the conditions, and the device will change the watering frequency using pulse width modulation. The user can change the display of the screen, using the button, to see the conditions inside the greenhouse. The device is battery powered and will go into sleep mode during the night to preserve battery life.

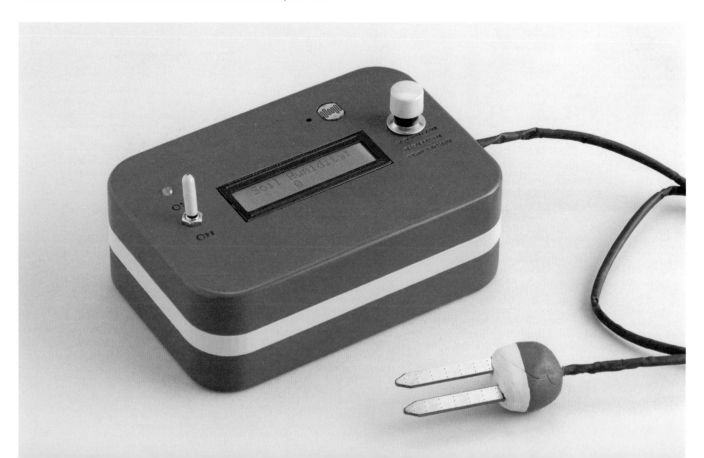

Seb Parker
Industrial Design and Technology BA

Powered Respirator

This is a powered air purifying respirator which assists the user's breathing by measuring mask pressure and adjusting fan speed to decrease breathing resistance for medical or industrial applications.

The system is intended for industrial or medical applications to improve user comfort over a long duration by reducing inhale and exhale resistance. This is achieved by measuring the mask pressure through the use of a differential pressure sensor and using the analogue signal to directly adjust the speed of the brushless electric ducted fan to maintain positive pressure. This reduces the chances of inhaling particles through mask leaks and increases mask comfort by reducing breathing resistance.

Air is fed to the mask from the back of the head via an FDM 3D printed flexible tube. The filters, motor and control circuitry are mounted on the back of the wearer's head for improved ergonomics. To power the system a belt mounted Lithium-ion battery pack was made with 12 '18650' cells.

A collaborative project with Avon Protection

Vasily Parshin
Product Design Engineering BSc

Low Ridah

An electric mobility scooter converted to use power steering and other features using a custom-made circuit and controlled via a joystick.

A retrofitted mobility scooter that is controlled via a single joystick & button. The scooter can carry up to 100kg and move in forward/reverse direction as well as steer. The user can interact with the device via the controller and a LCD display.

The PIC sends signals to 2 H-Bridges which control the high current from the battery going to the motors. The parameters such as relative speed and direction of turn can be read on the LCD. Going forward is possible using PWM which allows for speed control. Going backwards can only be done at full

speed - the user is prompted to check if it is safe to do so as a safety feature. The joystick button acts as an additional control for entering the user credentials at start of operation and as a buzzer during operation.

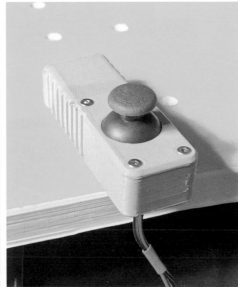

GRAPHIC DESIGN

Dr Dora Souza Dias
Lecturer in Design

In this academic year, the Advanced Graphic Communication module aimed to assist students in developing a repertoire of appropriate methodologies, theories and techniques to support their creative processes as well as to provide means for critical evaluation of visual communication products. The module also aims to allow students to develop a practical understanding of graphic design applications and of production processes and techniques for printed and digital products and media. Moreover, it was expected that students would develop an understanding of, and an ability to produce, graphic visual communications in a variety of media at a professional level.

This year's projects show a great range of focus, techniques and mediums. Each student was given the freedom to develop their own briefs which were supported by thorough research. The projects selected here demonstrate the quality of the work achieved by the students, from educational materials to travel apps.

Mia Alamo
Industrial Design and Technology BA

Home Trial Box for Glasses Direct

Re-design of the Home Trial Box for Glasses Direct focusing on creating abstract graphics based on the story of the product.

This collaboration with Glasses Direct comes from a need to re-design their Home Trial Box. The Home Trial Box as it stands is a service that allows the customer to try frames available from the convenience of their own home (essentially a try before you buy scheme).

This letterbox size package holds 4 frames and contains various advertising content inside. The outcome for this collaboration was to make the design more subjective to the company and incorporate art abstraction based on the story of the

frames themselves. The final design incorporates abstracted segments of the storyline in a seamless repeat pattern. Different tonal variations of the company's core colours have been layered to give more depth to the design. This style has been carried across the internal contents to create a refreshing aesthetic for the brand.

A collaborative project with Glasses Direct

Caitlin Beer
Industrial Design and Technology BA

Eat More Plants

Encouraging those who are skeptical of a vegan diet to eat more plant based meals through simple recipes offering nutritional guidance.

Despite the growing interest in plant based eating, many misconceptions still exist in relation to cost and maintenance of a nutritionally balanced diet preventing large sections of the population from considering a meat and dairy free diet. This reflects the need for further education in the variety of foods that are included in a plant based diet, and their nutritional values.

Deliberately steering away from an emphasis on the ethical issues usually associated with veganism, the Eat More

Plants campaign aims to inspire people to embrace a more plant based diet by providing them with accurate nutritional information and quick, easy to follow recipes. The goal is to motivate people to reduce their consumption of meat and dairy and demonstrate that essential nutrients can be effectively maintained within a plant based diet.

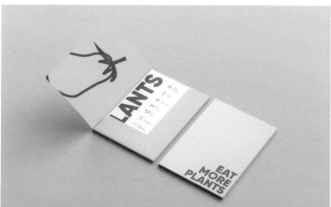

Arthur Brooks
Industrial Design and Technology BA

HolmBrew

The branding of a father/son owned home brewing company. Located in the county of Dorset, the brand reflects its rural heritage.

The branding for HolmBrew, from its core, follows the idea that a brand should tell a story. A visually unique yet pleasing graphic identity turns a home brewed beer into a marketable product. To do this the origins of the beer and the origins of the brand have been seamlessly woven together.

The 'Holm' in HolmBrew is taken from the name of the house where the beer has been brewed. The sheep's head logo has been inspired by the flock that the family herds and raises on their farm, and the name of each beer comes from the different breeds of sheep found around the UK countryside. With a classic retro design and grungy unpolished finish, HolmBrew is a toast to the unrefined and passion-filled beer it represents.

Imogen Campbell-Heanue
Product Design Engineering BSc

Fro Club

Fro Club is a hair workshop which aims to empower and inspire the Black community through hair education. Encouraging those to feel comfortable and confident rocking their natural hair!

Texturism is a form of discrimination which continues to oppress the Black community. There exists a social pressure to conform to Eurocentric beauty standards. Oftentimes, coily and kinky hair is deemed 'unattractive' and 'unprofessional'. This vilification of afro-textured hair causes many to feel ashamed of what naturally protrudes from their bodies, and consequently hair care is neglected.

Unfortunately, texturism is also known to create arbitrary barriers into professional environments. Fro Club aims to tackle texturism and empower the Black community. This workshop provides grooming education by demonstrating how hair health, for afro-textured hair, can be restored and maintained, whilst also creating a comfortable environment for individuals to express themselves judgement-free. This educational workshop provides a platform for an underrepresented hair demographic, celebrates the Black community and fosters a discrimination-free zone.

Niamh Cogley-Rock
Industrial Design and Technology BA

Fight Back

Fight Back is an App which digitalises Exposure Response Therapy, a form of CBT, acting as a lifelong treatment tool for OCD.

ERP has been found to be the most effective form of CBT with an 85% improvement rate for OCD. Fight Back provides the user with the framework to continue treatment throughout their lives. It tracks anxiety throughout tasks at different time intervals so the user can clearly identify patterns. It allows new tasks to be added and for steps to be adjusted based upon the user's preference. It also features goal setting statements, emergency contacts and archived tasks.

The logo and application have been designed to be as inconspicuous as possible to allow privacy when in use outside the home such as in public areas and schools. By providing the support and structure required by OCD sufferers, they can continue to fight back individually with the help of ERP and gain independence within their lives.

Hannah Coombs
Industrial Design and Technology BA

The Breathe Journal

An A5 journal containing 120 pages of activities and exercises aimed at improving your mental health. It is currently being sold online at www.HelloRecovery.co.uk.

The Breathe Journal is the perfect companion for anyone wanting to improve their mental health, whether diagnosed with a mental health condition or just wanting to keep healthy and happy. The journal contains guided exercises, coping strategies, distractions and activities aimed at improving your mental wellbeing. The colour palette and layout are designed to be both accessible and calming.

User research and testing was conducted with several young adults with depression and anxiety, the two most common diagnoses in this age group, to ensure the journal meets their needs and offers relevant support. The Breathe Journal was developed alongside Hello Recovery: Hannah's business selling handmade products aimed at improving mental wellbeing. The journal has been professionally printed on 120gsm uncoated stock, suitable for writing on, with luxury 350gsm silk covers. In the first month, over twenty journals were sold.

A collaborative project with Hello Recovery

Elise Filleul
Industrial Design and Technology BA

MYO (Make Your Own)

This animation and step by step guide encourages people to live a more sustainable lifestyle by making their own bio-plastic products.

The average American throws away 84 kg of plastic per year. 50 percent of the plastic we use, we use just once and throw away. Part of the solution to this environmental disaster is to change to biodegradable plastic.

MYO was developed to teach people how to make their own biodegradable plastic products using the step by step guide and moulds. Making bio-plastic products is a fun and creative pastime which enables the user to lead a more self-sufficient lifestyle and ease their eco-anxiety. The brand was developed

to appear playful and ecologically conscious. The animation was made to encourage people to try making bio-plastics. It was made with a cut out animation style that embodies the brand identity. The guide encourages further exploration of the potential uses of homemade bio-plastics.

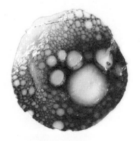

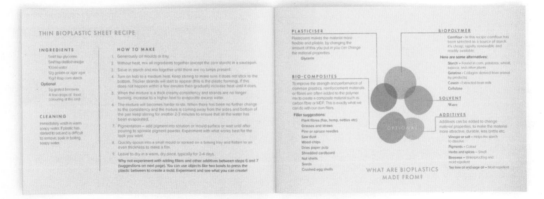

Megan King
Industrial Design and Technology BA

Fashion Unravelled

A campaign to educate consumers about the environmental and social impacts of their clothing, to drive a shift towards a more transparent fashion industry.

10% of all global carbon emissions are emitted by the fashion industry, a figure that outweighs the carbon footprint of all international flights. The majority of consumers are unaware of the massive impact their buying habits are having on the environment.

Fashion Unravelled is a disruptive campaign that provides customers with previously hidden information regarding the environmental and social impacts of the fashion industry. The campaign is not only to educate and empower consumers

but also to start a consumer driven change within the fashion industry as more consumers demand honesty from fashion brands. The campaign strives to educate more consumers ensuring they are informed about their garments and provides a platform for pressure to be placed on brands to become more transparent about their supply chains and carbon footprints going forward.

Nivedhaa Muthu
Product Design BSc

Artem

A personalised companion to empower and educate women on their journey through menopause, alleviate their menopausal symptoms and create a positive community to share and exchange their ideas and experiences.

Women's healthcare and wellbeing is anything but niche. Menopause is a natural phase in every woman's life, yet there is a lack of awareness and stigma attached to it. As every woman's menopause experience is unique, they don't know what to expect. With more than 34 symptoms, varying in severity and combinations based on the individual, women tend to endure menopausal symptoms silently.

Artem, your menopause companion, is a mobile application which provides a platform for women to develop a positive

attitude in understanding their bodies and feel confident. The app aims to create awareness by educating them about menopause and providing quick relief tips and strategies to enhance their quality of life. Artem assists by tracking symptoms, learning about lifestyle triggers and analysing trends. It breaks barriers and opens conversations, empowering women internally and externally.

Maria Alejandra Pinilla Pease
Industrial Design and Technology BA

glocal

glocal; making travel planning simple, smart and straightforward. Helping you spend less time planning your trips and more time enjoying them.

In the last few years, travel planning has become time consuming, overwhelming and tedious. Therefore, glocal has been created to help you plan and find the best activities to enjoy during your trips. In glocal you can find pre-made itineraries or create your own. Each itinerary can be fully personalised to fit your travel needs but we'll help you make the best decision.

Creating an itinerary is simple and fast, just select where you are going, for how long and your interests. You can also add

places which are already on your to-do list to make sure they are included in the itinerary.

Travel is a learning opportunity, therefore, within each itinerary you'll find key facts about different cultures in a bite-size form that will help you make the most out of every adventure.

Victoria Poizer
Industrial Design and Technology BA

Rubbish! Rubbish Everywhere

Rubbish! Rubbish Everywhere is a children's picture book that educates 3-5 year olds on the importance of sustainability and encourages them to tackle current problems through upcycling.

It is predicted that by 2050 the ocean will contain more plastic by weight than fish. Teaching children to upcycle from a young age can expose them to environmental issues of global relevance whilst encouraging their learning of the world around them and exploration of creative solutions. The act of story book sharing where parents read to their children, promotes the development of language and literacy abilities that will positively affect their academic success.

The story book combines these key issues as the reader is encouraged to think creatively and follow Jude on her upcycling journey as she makes discarded items into something useful. The aim is to inspire parents, teachers and children to get imaginative with how they regard their waste and the planet, whilst educating children on the benefits of upcycling and provoking sustainable change for future generations.

Katie Price
Industrial Design and Technology BA

Second Aid

A first-aid kit designed to support young businesses and their employees manage their mental health from within the workplace.

1 in 6 people in the UK are affected by mental health problems, often caused by, or accelerated within the workplace. Many businesses, particularly young companies and start-ups do not have the resources or budgets to invest in solutions and services which offer appropriate support for employees experiencing difficulties. This ultimately results in companies experiencing great financial losses and increased pressures as employees can become unable to work.

Second aid is a play on the idea of a first-aid kit, which are mandatory inside the walls of an office or workplace. Continuous research with a young company throughout the project duration lead to the design directions of the style, language and product artefacts which were discovered to be helpful to employees when looking out for themselves and their team.

Isaac Reeves
Product Design BSc

This Place In Time

Promoting the history and cultural significance of Brunel University London with a decentralised exhibition of photographic art, designed for maximum engagement even among the most apathetic campus users.

This Place In Time aims to improve the Brunel campus experience by utilising the university's rich history. The exhibition features a series of then-and-now photomontages, blending Brunel past and Brunel present into a single image. These aren't displayed in a gallery but they were originally taken as large scale floor stickers, allowing the user to stand in the shoes of the photographer and reimagine the space around them with a new depth of understanding. This decentralised layout means that it will be seen by almost all campus users, rather than just those who would seek it.

The exhibition is not solely artwork based however. Each image has a story, and the physical artefacts encourage the user to discover more with the accompanying web-app. This includes additional research and archive material for each image, as well as an exhibition map.

Natalia Rehakova
Industrial Design and Technology BA

Hunter Packaging

With only a handful of companies considering the disabled when designing packaging, Hunter focuses on creating an assortment of smart, intuitive, and colour-conscious solutions for the visually impaired and colour-blind.

Honey Hunter provides a solution for portioning honey in the form of gelatin encased balls for the visually impaired to easily gauge quantities through their sense of touch. Braille, the lid's honeycomb engraving and a smell-patch infused in ester methyl phenylacetate to emit a honey scent, were incorporated to engage the other senses.

Protein Hunter ensures easy accessibility through perforated cardboard and large tabs. Vacuum formed packaging exposes the nature of the product and its source, illustrated

by a pig cut-out. A real-time freshness bump indicator replaces the expiry label and ester pentyl acetate imitates the scent of apples.

Snack Hunter consists of an outer sleeve which can be removed, revealing an origami bowl for convenience. The nutritional traffic light system was adapted, integrating a 1-3 dot and wording system because red-green colour-blindness can lead to potential health risks.

Conor Richey
Industrial Design and Technology BA

Pollinator Planet

Pollinator Planet is a conceptual charity designed to raise awareness and conservation efforts for wild pollinators in UK cities. The charity is realised through a theoretical collaboration with Costa Coffee.

The world's pollinator population has seen a drastic decline in the last 25 years. The loss of pollinators could result in the loss of many common goods, such as coffee. It has become common to associate pollinator decline with bees; however, the issue is much more complex and involves thousands of species.

Pollinator Planet is a conceptual charity, which aims to raise awareness and educate the UK urban population on a wide range of wild pollinators, and how their decline impacts our

future. The project comes in the form of a brand identity for the charity, as well as a theoretical partnership with Costa Coffee. This partnership would deliver sustainable mugs, loyalty cards, and in-store messaging to millions of customers, spreading the message about wild pollinators and their decline to those who would be directly affected by it.

Costa Coffee were not engaged in any consultancy or collaborative capacity with this project. Any publicity is limited to personal, academic use.

Dante Roberts
Product Design BSc

areyoureallylistening?

Refocusing people on the only important aspect of music - sound, through hiding a track's popularity, genre and artist, to prevent any bias being formed against it.

The discovery of a new artist can be what helps start your interest into different genres, which can subsequently help you relate more with others whose music taste differs from your own.

areyoureallylistening? is a platform that makes music recommendations through prompting a user to enter their favourite artist, allowing it to ignore any music that is closely related to them. This is to increase the likelihood of a user listening to music they haven't heard before. Users are also

encouraged to select an emotion they want to evoke when listening, to further boost this likelihood. Once a user has listened to five tracks (for 30 seconds each), the platform generates a playlist which can then be added to a user's preferred music library.

Amber Sayers
Industrial Design and Technology BA

What's Your Excuse?

A campaign focused on how cervical screening attendance reached a 20-year low in 2019. It highlights excuses given by women and how they are not worth risking your life for.

At the heart of the campaign are the excuses and misconceptions of women, who have highlighted their struggles with attending smear test appointments. Barriers include embarrassment, body confidence, fear of the procedure and lack of awareness to name a few.

The aim is for others to identify and feel empowered by the messages and to attend an important life saving preventative test. The campaign brings a cheeky and thought-provoking perspective to an area of women's health that is largely

unspoken and taboo. By using eye catching photography that creates anatomical ambiguities and connotations, it aims to shock the audience and grab their attention. The campaign will help to spread awareness via a multitude of communication channels including posters, billboard adverts, information cards, a social media presence and age appropriate educational HPV leaflets.

Max Trafford
Product Design BSc

Turn Off Your Lights

As our planet continues to develop, light pollution is getting worse. Making people more aware of this problem is the next step in reducing our output of light.

Light pollution is directly affecting our planet's environment. It is a problem which is often ignored, overlooked or not even considered, but it is having serious implications. Currently, 83% of the world's population is living under skies that are at least 10% brighter than their natural, unpolluted state. You do not realise how bad light pollution is in London until you move here from an area which has minimal. This project was designed to address a problem that needed more awareness and attention.

Using night sky photos taken from dark sky locations, such as Dorset & Devon, these were photoshopped on to well-known locations in London. The aesthetic appeal of these images should make people realise what London could look like if there was less light pollution and take action.

..if you turn off your lights

www.earthhour.org
28th March - 8:30pm

60+
EARTH
HOUR

MSc DESIGN

MSc Intergrated Product Design

Dr Fabrizio Ceschin
Senior Lecturer in Design for Sustainability and Programme Director for MSc Integrated Product Design

In order to cope with the economic, social and environmental challenges we are facing nowadays, designers need to innovate beyond individual products and conceive systemic solutions blending physical and digital products, services, spaces and communication. Our MSc IPD degree focuses on the design of these innovative integrated solutions. In pursuing this, we emphasise the balance between the interest of users, industry, society and the environment. We cover the whole design process, integrating all aspects relevant to the development of these systemic solutions: human needs, sustainability, technology, aesthetics, management, marketing, business and design methods.

This programme is delivered by a cross-disciplinary lecturing team enhanced by design and branding professionals. Live briefs from small, medium and large enterprises from our industry collaborative partners are integrated in our modules and play a pivotal role in the learning experience. Our MSc programme is accredited by the Institution of Engineering Designers (IED) and is studied full-time over one year. As a result, we produce highly qualified and sought after designers who are employed in companies ranging from design consultancies, research and development departments to research institutions and government bodies.

MSc Sustainability, Entrepreneurship and Design

Dr Edwin Routledge
Reader

The Sustainability, Entrepreneurship and Design MSc has been developed to equip students with the practical and entrepreneurial skills required to deal with sustainability and environmental management issues in any business. They will be able to help address the next big challenges in society; to transform our economy to incorporate the principles of sustainability. This presents an exciting opportunity for them to be at the forefront of rethinking, redesigning and rebuilding a positive future for business practice. They'll be encouraged to infuse environmental awareness into societies and make tangible contributions to the theory and practice of environmental protection, sustainable business and a circular (green) economy.

This course entitles them to free student membership of the IEMA for the duration of the course and on successful completion, qualify for GradIEMA. Graduate membership is a launchpad for future leaders within environment and sustainability and offers a range of benefits to support them throughout their career.

Awards

The projects of Brunel students are often recognised by the design industry in the form of awards and prizes, and this year is no exception. On the MSc courses, these come as a result of both collaborative live briefs and independent competitions.

Glen Dimplex and Roberts Radio Live Project

This year, Roberts Radio and Glen Dimplex Design offered a live project to our MSc students as part of their Professional Design Studio module. This resulted in three winners and two commended entries, as well as a number of excellent projects. A prize of a Roberts Radio was awarded to the three winning entries.

Winners:

1st place - Zhenyu Yang - 'E-Scope'

2nd place - Han Hu - 'Energy Bucket'

3rd place - Binger Yu - 'Ring'

Commended students:

Shuyu Zhang - 'Triangle Speaker'

Chen Kong - 'Home Speaker Design'

RSA Student Design Awards

The RSA Student Design Award is an annual competiiton for higher education students and graduates. RSA's briefs are designed to focus on social, environmental and economic issues.

RSA hopes to empower a generation of savvy, employable designers that realise the benefits technology can bring to society.

Brunel's history of success in this competition continued this year, with two projects, Helena Buckoke's 'STEMideas' and Anouk Dijkman's 'CoolCity' earning each of them commendations.

Design Innovation in Plastics Competition

Established in 1985, Design Innovation In Plastics is now the longest running student plastics design award in Europe. It is a valuable opportunity for design students to make a name for themselves in this field.

Around 280 students from 20 universities register for the competition every year.

Integrated Product Design student Zihao Zhang won 3rd place in this year's competition for his 'Freefitness' design proposal, a device that joins plastic bottles together to form dumbbells. Zihao won a cash prize and a placement opportunity.

Helena Buckoke
Integrated Product Design MSc

STEMideas

A response to the RSA brief: How might we harness broad-leaved woodlands and their resources to increase their local economic, social and environmental value?

STEMideas is a STEM activity, where children are taken into their local woodlands by designers and taught about the environment and design process. Together, they co-design an area for their community, which is constructed by professionals, that will help them play whilst in woodlands.

Not only will this build a community space via a public recreation area, but will include both physical and mental health benefits from all the service's activities.

The system becomes circular, as the non-invasive construction of natural materials can be dismantled allowing the area

to return to its original state. Children will gain a "sense of ownership" for their creation and thus respect for the natural world, leading to further benefit to the environment.

Both the creative educational activities and resultant physical play area will allow this service to provide for a range of families.

Commended - RSA Student Student Awards 2020

Anouk Dijkman
Sustainability, Entrepreneurship and Design MSc

CoolCity

CoolCity is a multi-stakeholder program encouraging improved quality of life through urban climate-proofing. It supports people from a shared neighbourhood to co-finance green initiatives, led by smart-systems.

The CoolCity project was a response to the 'AI100' brief, which asked "How might we use AI to support people to reach a happy, meaningful and productive one hundred year life?"

On the long-term, health throughout one's life is greatly influenced by one's environment from an early age , and climate change is expected to increasingly exacerbate this. CoolCity tackles this challenge by providing urban residents across all ages with a healthier life environment while improving climate and social resilience. More specifically, it proposes a multi-stakeholder program that aims to improve quality of life by encouraging the co-financing and co-responsibility

of green projects. It does so by identifying greening opportunities, computing optimal greening plans and engaging relevant stakeholders to enable co-creation of new, nature infused, urban spaces.

Commended - RSA Student Student Award 2020

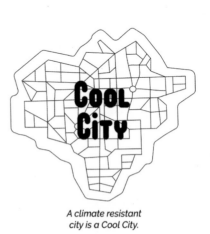

A climate resistant city is a Cool City.

José Dijkshoorn
Industrial Design Engineering BSc at TU Delft

Keith

Increasing the local economic, social and environmental value of broad-leaved woodlands – a personal guide made of wood thinnings, that will tell you the hidden stories of the woodland.

Managing woodlands is essential to maintain and enhance its biodiversity. Woodland management includes the removal of trees to allow other trees to grow. This process generates thinnings. Currently, hardwood thinnings are on the rise and they are almost exclusively used as fuel.

Keith is a portable woodland guide for visitors of all ages. He is made from hardwood thinnings and produced in the woodland. As you walk through the woodland, Keith will interact with you and will tell you about woodland management. He will explain why certain processes are needed to keep the woodland viable, such as the process of thinnings. Profits generated by Keith are reinvested back into the woodland.

Keith aims to educate, involve and inspire the local community and the visitors about the management of 'their' woodland in a fun way and so create a healthy woodland.

Hu Han
Integrated Product Design MSc

Sleeping Bird

Sleeping Bird is a night light that helps relieve people's insomnia. It helps people relax by connecting to mobile apps and using a group mutual assistance model on social platforms.

The product is mainly composed of 3 parts, plastic base, wooden branches and LED lights. The number of lights changes based on the number of friends the user has in the room in the app. Because it is magnetically mounted, it is very convenient to operate.

Users can set up or join others' virtual communities and set their own bedtime in the application. The night light is connected to the network. When you are ready to sleep, press the touch button on the product, you and the other users in your room will see the bird that represents you light up.

All online social networking is anonymous, and users can chat or leave messages online with other users. In addition, the night light can play natural sound effects that simulate the natural environment of the forest, helping users relax.

Chen Kong
Integrated Product Design MSc

Intuitive Home Speaker

Exploring a new form of a home speaker that surprises and delights customers by visualisation and tactile sound; considering the meaning of 'Britishness' and transforming it into the design.

"As humans, we have an inherent desire for stimulating experiences that can be achieved by exploring the world, connecting with others and feeling joy, wonder and delight." So why not explore the other possibility of music and sound?

Music can not only be heard but also be seen and touched. By combining the sensing technology, it is possible to visualize the sound by the 'antennas' which follow the music swing. Besides that, the product also explores how using intuitive interaction (natural gestures like swaying to control the speaker) can help the customers to use the speaker more naturally. Sensors detect the user's movement and an accelerometer measures

the movement, which work together to enable the user to control the speaker without looking. This way of operation will invite people's tactile interactions.

Created as part of the Roberts Radio & Glen Dimplex Design Live Project Competition

Yilei Lin
Integrated Product Design MSc

Book Reader

Book Reader scans books and plays their content. If connected to the Internet, it can also send audio or text messages to mobile phones, vehicle media and other devices.

With the advent of the internet, paper books are being used less frequently. However, paper books have a feeling that e-books cannot replace, and a large number of people like to feel the weight of the book they are reading. These people are often very busy and do not have time to sit and read. Book Reader aims to help those who like the feeling of a paper back book but are not able to spend the time reading. It can recognise the content of the book, and read it aloud when the user is busy performing other tasks such as house work.

The device can also display the text and images to users when they are less busy such as on their commute. Futhermore,

Book Reader can translate the contents of the book, greatly saving on manpower.

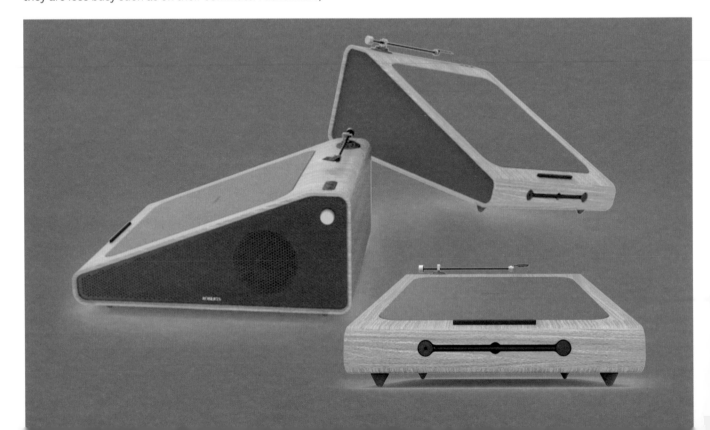

Hsin Lun Wu
Integrated Product Design MSc

On Air

On Air is a smart interactive media device with a tangible textual interface that registers the user interactions and makes it be wearable, for use whenever.

With the rise of cloud-based services and mobile devices, technology is breaking out of its shell. In order to dominate the audio market, products can not be over-complicated electronic devices. Moreover, the demand of the user also has to be considered.

According to the research, it outlines the thrilling potential of inclusive, multi-sensory, and exposes ways to extend the sensory richness of products, environments, and media. However, with the idea of audio-haptic immersion that tactile product reawakens a more sensual relationship with objects.

On Air is a new audio system that embeds a tactile surface and applies smart textiles. The aim of the project focuses on creating an audio product that is seamlessly integrated into daily life.

Created as part of the Roberts Radio & Glen Dimplex Design Live Project Competition

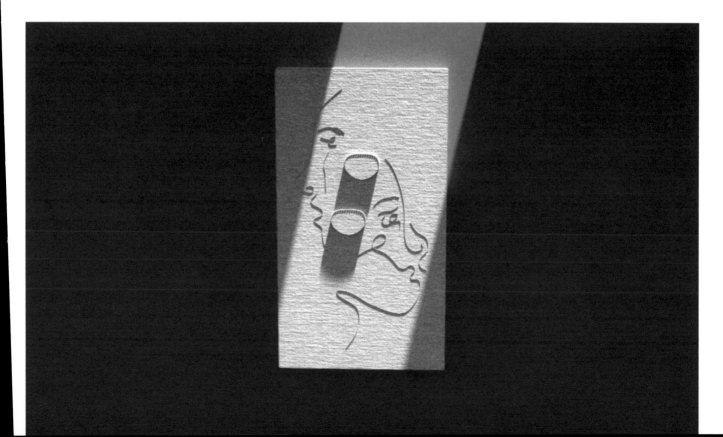

Khanh Mach
Sustainability, Entrepreneurship and Design MSc

SuperBelt

A child seat belt for modern families in big cities, opening access to public transport and restaurants for all children. SuperBelt - The super power to protect your child.

SuperBelt is a seat belt that can be clutched to a normal seat on public transport and coaches, fastened to restaurant chairs, attached to parent's arms and chairs for babies, and making it easy to carry them around.

SuperBelt is designed for urban families. The seat belt helps increase children's safety on public transport and in taxis, encouraging parents to take public transport while travelling with kids. It also allows children to engage more in family outdoor activities, boosting their development. The personal seat belt is more hygienic than shared high chairs.

The connecting pad with different animation character design can be customized to fit the child's interest, inspiring them to use seat belt frequently for their own safety. Recycled PET and aluminium used in this product share the same quality with virgin materials while prolonging the product life-span.

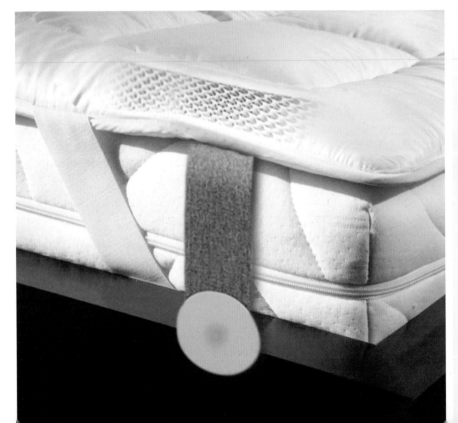

Kyle May
Integrated Product Design MSc

Roberts Rise

To create a new form of audio product for the British audio company, Roberts Radio, that constitutes Britishness with its design.

Roberts Rise is a home Hi-Fi system that incorporates old and new audio technologies, with the added controllable functionality of having the speakers rise up to the users' desired angle when in use, as well as lowering when turning off to provide a slim and minimalistic appearance. It includes old and new audio systems within, such as a Radio and a CD-Player, as well as modern wireless connectivity modules, such as Wi-Fi and Bluetooth; this provides flexibility for users, allowing them to play their desired audio-type through a single audio system.

With the addition of a Wi-Fi module, the speaker will be able

to connect to any smart device within the home, providing the possibility of creating a multi-device cinematic experience.

Created as part of the Roberts Radio & Glen Dimplex Design Live Project Competition

Junwen Qian
Integrated Product Design MSc

Robert Headphones

Using the principle of bone conduction, the product components can be changed modularly which allows users to easily switch between daily life and swimming.

The product is composed of upper and lower parts, and users can switch during swimming or daily use. When swimming, you can fix the headset on the strap of the swimming goggles. In daily life, you can use Bluetooth to link your mobile phone to the headphones. When swimming, Bluetooth doesn't have a good radiation range underwater, therefore, a built-in memory card can be used to access the user's favorite music without using Bluetooth when switching to swimming.The product's small size makes it easy to carry. The exterior

is made of frosted metal and a frosted plastic material, which is integrally formed without gaps or round holes, and has good

water resistance. The built-in battery can provide the power required for a swim.

Created as part of the Roberts Radio & Glen Dimplex Design Live Project Competition

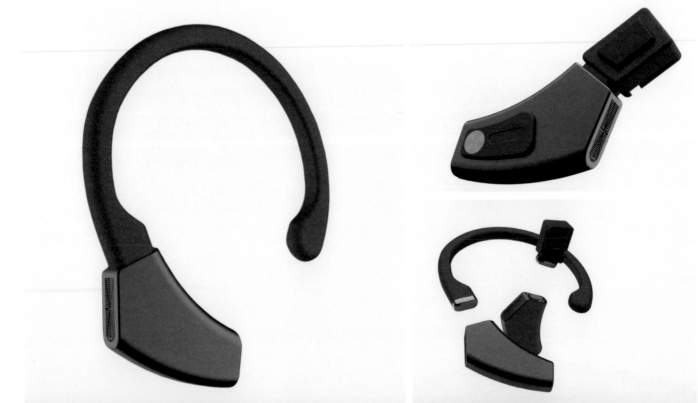

Leticia Suarez-Lamus
Sustainability, Entrepreneurship and Design MSc

ED - Electronic Detox

ED is an electronic detox station where people can leave their mobiles while enhancing quality time spent with loved ones, without the constant buzz of notifications.

The product offers a lifetime experience rather than just an interaction with a product. It is a statement of love and friendship in times where society is being constantly distracted by electronics and social media.

ED's design language and aesthetic are soft and friendly in order to attract people to see the product as cheerful and positive, rather than a punishment.

People's commitment to stop distractions or interruptions by their mobiles' notifications for one hour is a statement of love and friendship. It is an hour of full attention and immersion in an activity with the aim to improve relationships and to help improve people's attention span.

ED is not merely a product, but a life experience and a social statement.

Li-Yun Wang
Integrated Product Design MSc

Turn British

This is a live project with Roberts Radio, which aims to create a speaker with Roberts Radio's brand values and British aesthetics.

Turn British is not only a home loudspeaker, but also a home decoration that epitomises Britishness. It combines British architecture in terms of shape and pattern in a new user-interactive way which was inspired by the grandfather clock. The first grandfather clock was made by a British clockmaker in around 1680. The way to keep the clock working is to pull the weight up to the top regularly.

Turn British adopted this idea so that the user could change channel through dragging and turning the belt right or left, using the same action as keeping the clock working. Turn British could also be smart and remote-controlled. This not

only preserves the British culture of punctuality, but also retains the history and elegant appearance of a Roberts Radio.

Created as part of the Roberts Radio & Glen Dimplex Design Live Project Competition

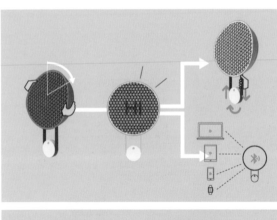

Xinpei Yang
Integrated Product Design MSc

Brunch Radio

A multi-functional and modular radio that can keep up with the demands of traditional British culture and be used in conjunction with other smart products.

The core of this radically redesigned product is the radio, designed to seamlessly integrate with other smart components which can be attached magnetically.

As well as a screen, camera and speakers, these modular components include: a voice recorder, with which the user can record meetings and more personal moments and add them to their 'Favourites' collection; a remote control, which can be used to change radio channels as well as control other components; and a timer which eases unnecessary panic when working under pressured conditions in an office. The timer can be set using the simple buttons, and an alarm will sound

through the radio speakers. The device can also be controlled wirelessly via bluetooth.

Created as part of the Roberts Radio & Glen Dimplex Design Live Project Competition

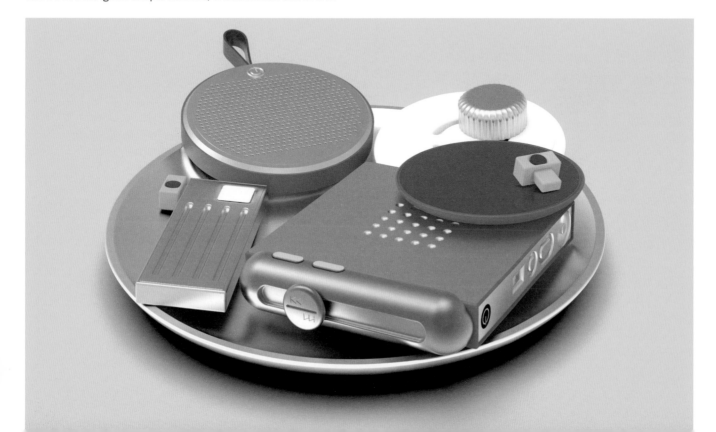

Zhenyu Yang
Integrated Product Design MSc

E-SCOPE

E-SCOPE is a portable device designed to further enhance user experience when using smartphones for study, work or leisure.

Since the beginning of the 21st century, the rise of smartphones and mobile networks have rapidly changed all aspects of people's lives. The explosive growth of mobile media content is becoming mainstream, and it is also becoming the main medium for people to exchange and experience information. However, the screen size and sound quality of mobile devices could be improved to meet the needs of users who want to create immersive experiences and share content.

Therefore, the designer considers integrating the two elements to form a portable media enhancer which includes a small projector and two speakers. The components are connected by a magnetic bayonet, and the users can easily separate the two speakers and connect them to the mobile via Bluetooth. Whether it's an occasional small meeting or browsing mobile media resources with friends, the content of mobile devices can be amplified.

1st Place - Roberts Radio & Glen Dimplex Design Live Project Competition

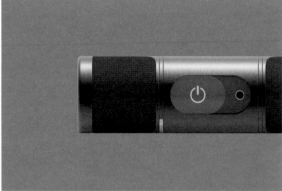

Binger Yu
Integrated Product Design MSc

Ring

Combining radio with fashion. The round shape forms a visual contrast with the old fashioned British satchel; which can be hungon the bag to make the satchel look more modern.

This is Roberts radio live project.   The design in the scene of the Mulberry handbag brand, was used to integrate 'Britishness' fashion into this design concept.

 The leather bags, suitable for students and office workers with 'Britishness', are square in shape, the radio is designed as a round shape, which makes the combination of the radio and bag look more fashionable and relaxed.

It uses the twisted way to open and close so that it can be hung on the bag safely.

The materials used are a combination of metal, leather and textile, which can change the colour of the appearance according to the customer's requirements. The speaker part is textile, the outer is decorated with leather, and the twisted opening and closing part is metal. These materials were chosen based on the features of the existing products of Roberts radio brand.

3rd Place - Roberts Radio & Glen Dimplex Design Live Project Competition

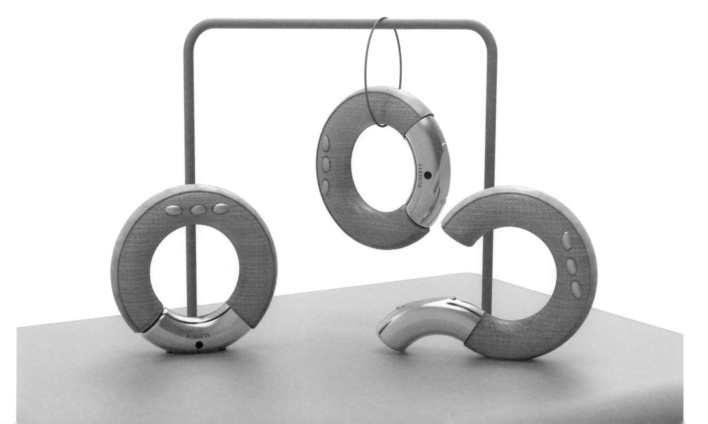

Shuyu Zhang
Integrated Product Design MSc

Triangle Speaker-Fold and Wall

The Triangle Speaker Fold uses soft materials to allow the speaker to change its shape freely. Tringle Wall's modular design makes it easy to customise the colour combination and pattern.

How can you make speakers 'invisible' at home? The Triangle Fold and Wall series are a set of home speakers, which are controlled by mobile phone via Bluetooth.

The design is inspired by the shape of brickwork in British architecture. The magnet inside the Fold helps the speaker change into different shapes, freely allowing the speaker to be placed on various surfaces, such as sofa armrests, without taking up excess space.

The modular design of Wall allows the user to adjust each module and customise the colour combination and pattern. It is easy to add or replace each module to fit the indoor environment and is suitable to hang on the wall as house decoration.

Commended - Roberts Radio & Glen Dimplex Design Live Project Competition

Zihao Zhang
Integrated Product Design MSc

FREEFITNESS

FREEFITNESS is a budget and environmental-friendly device that fits plastic bottles together to form dumbbells.

FREEFITNESS can be continuously and simply used at home. The target users for this product are busy citizens who do not have time to go to gym or complete any exercise.

The benefits of FREEFITNESS are: time saved as the user is able to complete exercises anywhere, at home or work; low cost, saving the user money on professional gym equipment; a wide variety of exercises; and a reduced environmental impact, using plastic bottles which would otherwise be wasted.

This product can be shared, reused, refurbished and recycled throughout the stages of the technosphere circular economy.

The product is manufactured from high-density polyethylene (HDPE) using injection moulding processes. The textured surface of the device provides a grip for the user ensuring safe usage. The cost of the product is £8.09.

3rd place - 2020 Design Innovation in Plastics (DIP) competition

MA

DESIG

MA Design and Branding Strategy

Dr Busayawan Lam
Senior Lecturer in Design Innovation

MA Design and Branding Strategy prepares students for a career of leading, designing and managing brands at the highest strategic level. Students who have graduated from this course go on to work globally for admired major and challenger brands, prestigious brand agencies and top-level creative consultancies. Many also start and run their own successful businesses. The course aims to explore branding from a design perspective. It extensively presents and analyses famous and emerging brands, brand trends and brand models.

Workshops play a major part in the teaching experience and it is here that students practically engage with contemporary brand issues and tools. Opportunities to develop specialisms in areas such as luxury branding, place branding, digital branding, fashion branding and social branding are encouraged and in many of those areas, Brunel Design has pioneered new thinking. We actively engage with the London and International brand community with an impressive list of leading brand and design experts regularly talking to students or facilitating workshops and other activities. This course is generally considered the first Design Branding Master's programme globally and continues to pioneer content.

MA Design Strategy & Innovation

Dr Busayawan Lam
Senior Lecturer in Design Innovation

MA Design Strategy & Innovation aims to give designers and other creative disciplines the skills and knowledge to utilise design thinking and to leverage design in the pursuit of strategic organisational change and improvement in private and public sectors as well as not-for-profit organisations. Graduates from this course often pursue careers in innovation from both consultancy and client positions.

The programme explores how design can be a catalyst for various types of innovation – e.g. new products and services, new processes, new ways of managing creative teams and collaborating with stakeholders. The students will learn how to evaluate user needs and market demand and discuss key factors influencing innovation development, such as digital economy, collaborative economy and social responsibility. They also investigate future scenarios and emerging practices in the field of design and innovation in order to develop strategic appropriate directions for innovation and innovation culture. We actively engage with pioneers in the field of design and innovation. They are regularly invited to give lectures and run workshops and seminars with students. Students are also given opportunities to engage with on-going externally funded research projects.

Ellen Jenkin
Design and Branding Strategy MA

Place Branding & Experience

An investigation into how place branding and experience design can revive UK high streets through discovering the identity of places and creating experiences to enforce identity and improve community wellbeing.

For over a decade the high street has been significantly impacted by a shift in consumer habits. Places that once used to be bustling with trade, are now desolate areas filled with boarded-up storefronts and closing-down sales. This project aims to develop a place branding strategy for UK high streets, with implementation of experiential design, to improve the consumer's experience of high streets, and therefore increase footfall. The project will explore the wants, needs and expectations of high street consumers, as well as using expert opinions to gain insight into what needs to happen to improve high streets from a practical point of view. To support the

findings will be an extensive literature review, which focuses on theory and the effectiveness of place branding and experiential design, plus the relationship between the two. A community-centric approach instead of meeting economic demands could pose as a more sustainable long-term solution rather than a quick fix that is not maintained.

Haifa Kadhem
Design, Strategy and Innovation MA

Design for SMEs in Bahrain

Promoting strategic design to support the growth and innovation of Bahrain's small to medium enterprises.

Over the next few years Bahrain aims to shift focus from oil wealth towards a diversified economy, by supporting the growth of the private sector. Despite Bahrain's efforts to grow the private sector, SMEs overwhelmingly dominate the market and only contribute 30% to the GDP. Due to the narrow view of design value in business, it has not been used effectively as a solution to support SMEs sustainable growth and instigate innovation in Bahrain. Design has a positive correlation between innovation and economic growth, and it has been used by various countries including the UK, Singapore, South Korea and Denmark as a strategic tool to add a competitive advantage to domestic products and services and transform businesses. Consequently, The aim of the research is to develop a guideline to promote the strategic use of design by SMEs in Bahrain to support growth and instigate innovation.

HeeSu Lee
Design and Branding Strategy MA

Innovation of CX

How can South Korea based business-to-consumer (B2C) companies create compelling 'Experiential Consumer Communications' integrated with IT emerging technologies whilst enhancing the role of design as integrator?

Customers want to purchase psychological and sociocultural experiences, not just observing products and their functions. Design-driven innovation with breakthrough technologies guide them to the world of compelling experiences. Leading companies in the global market valued the role of designers and viewed design as an overall corporate management strategy. In the era of the Fourth Industrial Revolution, researchers suggest that technology- and emotion-based evaluations should be applied. South Korea, while renowned as a high-tech country with rich advanced technology and large scale R&D, lags behind global companies in brand competitiveness. This project will discuss problems and opportunities of strategic design and innovation practices from Korea originated B2C companies with experts from IT, design and advertising industries. It also looks into the new normal and the trend of consumer communications in this era. Lastly, it aims to create a design led innovation framework which is suitable for the business infrastructure of Korea, developed with opinions and evaluations delivered from experts.

Alejandro Romero Rosell
Design Strategy and Innovation MA

Sublime Immersive Experiences

The project explores how the user experience of immersive technologies (VR, AR & MR) can be enhanced using precepts from immersive and transmedia storytelling at the National Gallery.

The National Gallery in London is interested in immersive technologies, namely VR, AR & MR. The lack of widespread usability standards challenges the design of immersive experiences, and users often suffer from dizziness, FOMO, puzzlement and hardship readapting to the real environment. Avoiding such perils does not rely solely on technology. Storytelling has proven to support the creation of mental models that help users better navigate virtual spaces. However, immersive storytelling is still in its infancy and user agency inside the virtual space challenges narrative coherence.

The current project aims at developing a framework that

strategically integrates user experience and storytelling principles as modular design heuristics. They will take episodic form across several touch-points of the user journey. Moreover, these rules of thumb will regulate emotional granularity and agency to keep the user engaged while being subtly guided. The stories of the artworks at the National Gallery have the substance to design sublime immersive experiences.

A collaborative project with the National Gallery

Yiting Zhu
Design and Branding Strategy MA

Everyday Aesthetic Appreciation

Developing a design-led strategy for Chinese authentic lifestyle brands, helping them stand out in the Chinese market and promote the value of distinctive Chinese aesthetics through brand experience.

The 11th Five-Year Plan of the Peoples Republic highlighted the need to "move from made in China to designed in China" - generating creativity is more valuable in the 21st-century economy, which require creative citizenship now more than ever. There is a strong link between citizens' aesthetic ability and creativity. Aesthetics are not the goal of creativity, but it are one of its essential components. As the increasingly prevalent phenomenon of the aestheticisation of life indicates, the aesthetic has a significant power to influence - and sometimes determine - the quality of life and society. China is trying to build a creative society and cultivate creative citizens to enhance its national power on a cultural level. Therefore, in this economic, political and cultural context, it is a good opportunity to develop local lifestyle brands in China. This project concludes by illustrating how such a practical lifestyle branding strategy provides new ways of enhancing lifestyle brands' experience to develop creative Chinese citizens with distinctive aesthetic appreciation.

PhD DESIGN

Dr Eujin Pei
Director of Postgraduate Research

Our design research at PhD level challenges doctoral researchers to become fully independent learners with a specialisation. The duration of study is usually three years of full-time study for the standard route, or four years for the integrated PhD programme. Each student is supported by a Principal Supervisor, a Secondary Supervisor and a Research Development Advisor, as well as through workshops organised by the College and the Graduate School. This is also enriched by regular seminars and talks hosted by the department, as well as through external conferences. The department also organises an annual design doctoral symposium that provides a platform to promote networking opportunities and to engage in panel discussions with academics that support future career development. In addition, social events that are held across the year create a more vibrant research culture. One of the most common reasons to undertake a doctoral degree is to pursue an interest for a subject and to contribute to new knowledge.

While a doctoral study requires commitment, it can be a fulfilling journey. The qualification opens new professional opportunities in research or knowledge-based sectors in academia as well as in the design and engineering industry. We also welcome applicants who wish to pursue practice-based research that would still contribute to new knowledge. We have three main intake dates across the year, in January, April and October. If you are interested to find out more, please get in touch with us. We would be happy to listen to you and provide information.

Youmna Abdel-Qader Al-Dmour
youmnaabdel-qaderatawi.al-dmour@brunel.ac.uk

Workplace Biophilic Design

This project seeks to develop a Toolkit to improve the quality of indoor workspaces using Biophilia.

Buildings in large densely populated cities have a potential to become joyful, cheerful and soulful spaces for people to live and work. For individuals to thrive and flourish for living or work, there is a need to capture the holistic environment of the building design as well as to enhance the user experience.

This project seeks to evaluate the Indoor Environment Quality and to understand how it affects the occupants' health, well-being and productivity.

This research analyses the work of the "Second Home" company which uses the concept of Biophilia by bringing nature to the inside of the building by adding large numbers of plants and to further propose that biophilia can potentially solve issues such as thermal comfort, air quality, acoustics, lighting and the office layout.

Qais Ahmad
qais.ahmad@brunel.ac.uk

Influencing Household Behaviour Towards Food Waste Prevention in Jordan

The aim of this project is to use design for behaviour change and communication design to develop a communication campaign to shape the behaviour of households around food waste reduction in the Jordanian context.

Our earth is currently facing many environmental, social, economic and ethical issues today. A major challenge that faces the international community is to provide safe food for over 9.1 billion people by the year 2050. Furthermore, one-third of the globally produced food is wasted according to the Food and Agriculture Organization of the United Nations. During the last decade, food waste has become an international concern to policymakers, practitioners, and researchers across a range of academic disciplines.

Jordan does not have a national solid waste management policy and disposes food waste directly into unsanitary landfills. The country's food waste generated per capita sometimes exceeds 210 kg per year and the overall aim of this research is to understand the current behaviour patterns of local households and to develop a communication campaign to shape a more socially responsible behaviour of households around food waste reduction in West and East Amman, Jordan.

Laila al-Jahwari
laila.al-jahwari@brunel.ac.uk

Using Immersive Virtual Reality in Product Design Processes for Design Practice and Education

This research aims to understand how immersive virtual technology can be used to improve cognitive processes in product design education and practice

In the new global economy, innovative techniques have a potential to shorten and accelerate the new product development process. This has become a necessity for product designers wanting to keep pace with changes in the marketplace.

One of these technologies include the use of immersive virtual reality. Despite the fact that immersive technologies have been widely researched, accepted and employed across various industries such as engineering and automotive design, there is limited research on the application of immersive technologies for small-scale products in design-based companies, and particularly for design education.

For this research, the data collection and analysis process will comprise of scenarios in both education and practice through three stages: exploration, in-depth research, and co-design and evaluation. The study will investigate aspects of design thinking, product design and the integration of immersive virtual reality technologies.

Mathurada Bejrananda
mathurada.bejrananda@brunel.ac.uk

Design-led Social Participation for Value Co-creation for the Thai OTOP Policy

This research suggests the use of participatory design principles with value cocreation processes to encourage local people to engage and enhance social innovation from a bottom-up approach.

The Thai OTOP (One Tumbon – Tumbon means subdistrict, One Product) policy was aimed at developing the local economy through local products using local resources. The current top-down approach was implemented without a clear sustainable plan as it focuses on the economy rather than the community's endogenous structure.

This research has identified an opportunity for a bottom-up approach by introducing participatory design in value co-creation where local voices can be heard and efforts integrated at a strategic level to make this system relevant for local needs. The research also uses participatory design and service design to support collaboration among stakeholders through social capital and community building activities.

Aimone Bodini
aimone.bodini@brunel.ac.uk

Virtual Production in Audio-visual Industry

A traditional indie-filmmaker cantered immersive digital tool for pre-production with an emphasis on real-world location in previsualization.

Immersive technologies such as Augmented and Virtual Reality are impacting more and more businesses and people across a broad variety of disciplines. In the audio- visual industry, immersive technologies have proved to be a valuable tool during the Virtual Production (VP) process.

Movies that involve the use of Computer-Generated Imagery (CGI) such as "Ready Player One" or "The Lion King" rely on the adoption of VP because among its many benefits, it allows directors and the film crew to visualize and capture places and scenes that do not exist or which would require an incredible amount of resources.

The concept behind VP is the real-time data exchange between the physical and virtual world with use of a real-time engine such as Unity or Unreal. As immersive technologies keep advancing and maturing at a fast pace, this research aims to exploit the commercial and creative opportunities that are being presented.

James Burchill
james.burchill@brunel.ac.uk

Building Better Communication

This framework aims to communicate radically innovative materials to designers, improving their likelihood of using it in their work and being able to create new applications.

This research investigates how radical innovations in material science can be better communicated to designers. In particular, it focuses on how language can be used to ensure that designers create feasible concepts when they are first introduced to a new material.

Results from user studies and workshops found that designers struggle to use existing tools to reliably create new ideas. Half of the designers failed to create feasible ideas. To produce a framework that would guide them, further tests were conducted through interviews and a thematic review to understand the language that designers use to communicate. Focus groups and surveys found that designers had a preference for certain words, language and sentence structure. A final workshop found that 84% of the ideas created by the designers using the framework became feasible. The value of the framework was further validated by reviewing it with industry and academic experts who saw this as a valuable tool to effectively communicate the material properties to designers.

Giselle Hsiang Loh
hsiang.loh@brunel.ac.uk

The Application of 4D Printing for Thermo-Responsive Textiles

This research investigates how 4D Printing and Functionally Graded Additive Manufacturing can create stimuli-responsive textiles with shape-changing abilities when subject to changes in temperature.

4D Printing (4DP) is defined as the use of Additive Manufacturing (AM) to produce stimuli-responsive parts that can transform from one form to another when subject to an external stimulus, without electro-mechanical devices. We also define Functionally Graded Additive Manufacturing (FGAM) as a layer-by-layer fabrication process achieved by intentionally modifying the process parameters and gradationally varying the spatial deposition of material organization within a single component to meet an intended function.

This research examines the state of the art of 4D Printing (4DP) and Functionally Graded Additive Manufacturing (FGAM),

clarifying their differences and determining the most suitable AM process for the creation of shape-changing thermo-responsive textiles. The key research areas include proposing a framework to select commercially available shape memory polymers suitable for 4D Printing; establishing a methodology for direct material extrusion onto textile substrates to create polymer-textile composites; and investigating key build and design parameters that will have the greatest influence over geometrical deformation of the textile.

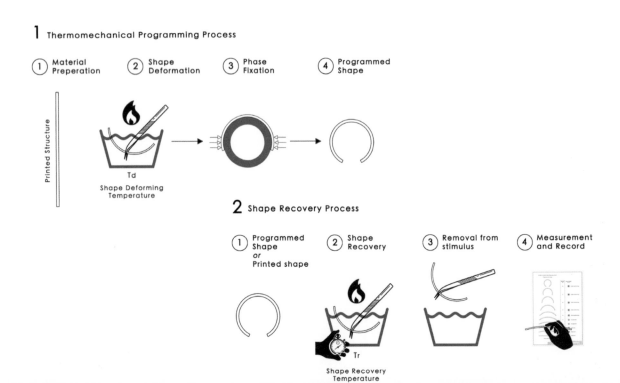

1 Thermomechanical Programming Process

Printed Structure

① Material Preperation ② Shape Deformation ③ Phase Fixation ④ Programmed Shape

Td
Shape Deforming Temperature

2 Shape Recovery Process

① Programmed Shape or Printed shape ② Shape Recovery ③ Removal from stimulus ④ Measurement and Record

Tr
Shape Recovery Temperature

Yuan Long
yuan.long@brunel.ac.uk

Design Product Service Systems applied to Reusable Packaging Systems

Reducing the total amount of plastic packaging waste with the consideration of businesses and consumers' behaviour.

Environmental sustainability is under the threat of excessive single-use plastic packaging which current waste management has failed to address. This research seeks to define a solution that can potentially curb packaging waste without sacrificing existing social needs.

Reusable packaging systems (RPSs) represent a circular approach to close the loop of consumption in which packaging can stay longer in the system yet satisfying social needs. However, the implementation of reusable packaging is limited. Product-Service Systems (PSSs) is widely regarded as a sustainable business model innovation for embracing circular consumption. As a result, applying PSSs to RPSs could potentially be used to address this issue. As there is limited knowledge regarding widespread adoption, this research aims to understand how to effectively apply PSSs to RPSs to support professionals addressing the packaging crisis in the food and household product industry.

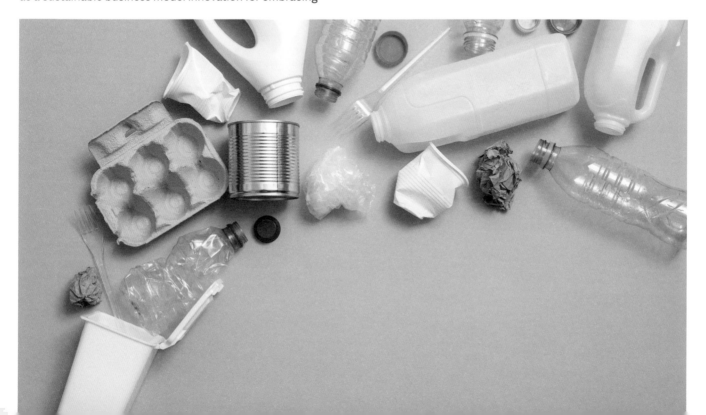

Gabriel Mothibedi
gabriel.mothibedi@brunel.ac.uk

Design Innovation in Botswana Through a National Design Strategy

This study envisions the implementation of a strategic design innovation policy for industrial development in Botswana through a national design capacity.

The ever-increasing rates of socio-economic advancements have resulted in a complex world of high global competition and demands for quality products and services. As such, design innovation has become a key economic development strategy leading to nations introducing design policies in order to transform their economic growth strategies into support programmes for resource management and value addition through design.

The focus of this study is a national design policy for industrial development, aiming at seeking potential applications of a design policy to enhance industrial development, through the support of SMEs in Botswana. The study also aims to promote design innovation as an economic development strategy, to encourage design adoption and support for SMEs, to enhance the quality of design curricula in higher education and to strengthen professional practice of design to achieve business and economic development objectives. The study envisions the implementation of a strategic national design policy of high level, in government through the Ministry of Investment, Trade and Industry.

Seokwoo Nam
seokwoo.nam@brunel.ac.uk

Programming 4D Printed Parts using Shape-Memory Polymers and Computer-Aided Design

This project investigates how Shape Memory Polymers (SMPs) can be programmed through the design of features using CAD to achieve expected shape-change behaviours.

Additive Manufacturing (AM) has been recognized as an innovative technology for future manufacturing systems. AM technology has made considerable progress in the use of materials, machines and processes with its great potential to change many things from everyday life to industrial products. In recent years, 4D Printing (4DP) has attracted widespread attention as a new technology to overcome the limitations of AM.

4D Printing is defined as a layer-by-layer manufacturing process to produce parts that are able to change its shape or assemble itself into a new configuration over time.

This project provides an understanding of shape change behaviour and structures that can be achieved through 4D Printing. It also explores how the use of Computer-Aided-Design (CAD) can influence the shape change effect. The outcome of this research provides designers and engineers an understanding of the potential use of predictive behaviour that can be realized using 4DP and for designers and engineers to implement appropriate design strategies.

Co-Innovate

Innovation is a key business growth mechanism. However, without the right expertise, knowledge and resources in place, creating a new product or service or even introducing a new process or technology is inherently risky. Co-Innovate is a business support service based at Brunel Design and jointly funded by Brunel University London, the European Regional Development Fund and the Greater London Authority.

Consisting of two interrelated programmes: Brunel Co-Innovate Journeys and Bridging the Gap, the service directly helps London-based SMEs and graduate entrepreneurs launch, grow and scale their innovation activities, while mitigating risk by connecting them with Brunel's world-class facilities and knowledge resources. Companies interested in working with Co-Innovate can benefit in a number of ways - from engaging with students on collaborative projects to address real-world business challenges, innovation mentoring, help to apply for project funding, tailored input from specialised academics, business growth training workshops to networking events.

If you are interested in exploring how Co-Innovate can help your business expand through innovation, please get in touch at **co-innovate@brunel.ac.uk** to speak to one of our Innovation Directors.

Design Plus

Design Plus is an ongoing design support programme by Brunel Design - focused on promoting and developing collaboration between the department and industry with an emphasis on design innovation and knowledge exchange. The programme is targeted at medium-size businesses, large corporations and public sector organisations – both nationally and internationally.

Brunel's industrial design, product design, product design engineering and design strategy programmes are amongst the highest-rated in the UK. Since 2004, students and academics from these programmes have applied their creativity and knowledge in collaborative design projects for a wide variety of companies, including Brompton Bikes, Hornby, British Telecom, JLR, several hospital trusts and many more.

Design Plus projects involve working with clients on the design and development of radical new ideas for products, services and processes. Students work individually or in small teams, supported and guided by their supervising tutor, to deliver design solutions of a very high standard. A Design Plus project is an opportunity both to access fresh thinking and to add considerable value to the collaborating student's education and career prospects.

If you have a real-life design challenge, we could help you gain a competitive advantage. To discuss collaboration opportunities, please get in touch at **designplus@brunel.ac.uk**.

Design+

Central Research Laboratory

CRL is the UKs leading accelerator and co-working space for hardware start-ups and product pioneers. It has supported hundreds of entrepreneurs to launch and scale their companies through product development, commercial strategy, prototyping, mentorship and access to a network of investors, mentors and partners.

Based at The Old Vinyl Factory in Hayes West London, CRL helps Brunel graduates and alumni who want to turn their product and technology ideas into a new business. CRL runs a six-month accelerator programme supporting early growth stage product pioneers. Six companies are selected to take part in an intensive support programme focused on product development and design, commercial and growth strategies and investor readiness.

Brunel alumni to go through the CRL accelerator programme include; Cosi Care, Aceleron, Mimica, Wase and Pet Instincts who have gone on to win multiple awards and raise millions of pounds.

CENTRAL
RESEARCH
LABORATORY

Santander Universities

Santander Universities' partnership with Brunel University London launched in 2014, since then we have helped to deliver life changing experiences to students through a range of scholarships, grants and start-up awards for student led businesses. Our programme has benefited hundreds of Brunel students with international mobility awards, scholarships, internships, whilst also supporting multiple student entrepreneurs and local SMEs with direct and indirect financial support.

Through Brunel's incubator at the Central Research Laboratory, we have provided direct monetary assistance to over a dozen Brunel start-ups, by providing equity-free seed funding grants, networking opportunities and part-funded internships. Santander Universities continues to be deeply embedded in the wider enterprise activity at Brunel, including the Made in Brunel awards, Venture Competition and the Co-Innovate business pitches. Given that the quality of enterprise education at Brunel is so strong, it should be no surprise that In 2018 and 2019, Brunel start-ups won the annual Santander Universities Entrepreneurship Awards!

Design Factory Global Network

This year, Brunel University London joined Design Factory Global Network (DFGN, dfgn.org), as the first higher education institution in the UK to obtain the network membership. DFGN is a worldwide association of 31 design-led innovation hubs at universities and research organisations across Europe, North America, South America, Asia and Australia.

The participation of Brunel in the network is managed by Brunel Design and the innovation hub at the campus in Uxbridge – dubbed Design Factory London - will be established in the new Teaching and Learning Centre building. Headed by Aalto University in Helsinki, Finland, with the members including CERN, University of São Paulo, Kyoto Design Lab and Swinburne University, DFGN promotes design thinking and interdisciplinary project-based learning through international student-led collaborative projects with major companies. The membership in DFGN enables Brunel Design students to work on live project briefs with their peers and industry at a global scale, thus greatly contributing to student experience, while the UK-based companies have the opportunity to collaborate not only with Brunel, but with an international community having an established track-record of fostering the culture of radical innovation.

If you are interested to hear more about Design Factory Global Network and explore the collaboration options, please contact us at dfgn@brunel.ac.uk.

IMPACTING BUSINESS BY DESIGN | + + +

Impacting Business By Design

In a world where business growth and competitiveness are becoming increasingly hard to realise, SMEs have been widely encouraged to adopt innovation as a growth mechanism. However, research into innovation success shows that for SMEs especially, innovation is often fraught with a variety of risks and challenges.

Picture the following: you are an SME and have identified a market opportunity or perhaps you want to develop a new product or service, even finance your product through a crowd-funding strategy. You are aware that innovation has some risks and your own company capability has some significant gaps and that to accomplish your goals you need the access to some specialised design or manufacturing expertise.

Imagine then, having available to you some of the UK's most substantial design and innovation resources to help you, a place where access to specialised expertise, knowledge and innovation funding opportunities is possible, and importantly, a place where commercial collaboration with SMEs is welcomed.

Impacting Business by Design is that place, a funded product innovation support programme set up to help entrepreneurs and product innovators by providing professional expertise in design, CAD, design for manufacture, engineering and product design, directly from Brunel University London.

Grant funding is provided for successful applicant companies to cover the costs of professional product development teams based within each of the three partner universities delivering this programme: Brunel, De Montfort and Nottingham Trent. These teams provide hands on design and development help for products in a range of sectors from consumer, med-tech, industrial, sports equipment, wearable technology, children's products and digital electronics products. Grants provided are only ever repaid, once the new product is successfully launched and generating a significant level of revenues.

To date, Impacting Business by Design has worked with a wide variety of companies from early stage start-ups to established businesses, all of whom are, for the first time, getting the opportunity to have a professional level of design and development expertise working on their product design project. These collaborations have resulted in new products, patents and hundreds of thousands of pounds of further investment being realised by participating businesses.

To find out more about this programme and get in touch, please visit: www.ibbdesign.co.uk

Clive Gee, a very special Made in Brunel champion

Made in Brunel has evolved to become the brand of Brunel Design, a cornerstone of the College of Engineering, Design and Physical Sciences and a University-wide symbol of student excellence. Behind this unique brand is a project champion, a remarkable, quiet, intelligent, focused individual, Clive Gee.

We moved Design from Runnymede campus to Uxbridge in 2004 and began to plan our strategy to mark our arrival; a new force to be reckoned with, a department full of passionately motivated students. It's fair to say we didn't have many friends at first; we were the newly adopted 'creative oddballs' who were somehow part of the School of Engineering and Design. In the old Wilfred Brown Building was the Development Office, a place where a team of charismatic individuals managed Brunel's Alumni communications, Graduation ceremonies, conferences and external events to fly Brunel's flag. The Development Office contained new friends and Clive Gee was one of this special group of people who brightened up one's day. He loved our Design students. This was the beginning of a symbiotic relationship to promote Design and Brunel.

In 2005 we were told to settle into our new cubbyhole on Uxbridge campus, tow the line, stop having shows and stuff, stop making books of our students' work, etc. So, we decided to create a brand, plan a big show and set about producing a new book, confidently announcing our arrival at Uxbridge. We called this new brand "*sharper" and held our first show in the newly built Bannerman Centre. Kitty Chisholm (then Director of Development) and her No.2, Clive Gee, came to see us, the work and our book. Following the show, 'senior management' told Design we should never do this again. Our knuckles were well and truly rapped. Thou shalt never make a song and dance here!

So, over the following year, we came up with a new idea, a bigger one... one so big that it would be shockingly unstoppable, a new brand, and - here's the genius – a brand not for Design but for the School of Engineering and Design. This brand would represent excellence, entrepreneurship, student empowerment and commercial awareness; everything that Brunel himself would have endorsed.

This new brand would be a School-wide venture; linking Design with all the Engineering departments, instantly representing the heart of Brunel University. We launched MADE IN BRUNEL.

And our dear friends Kitty and Clive were there right from the start, providing support, guidance, wisdom and managerial advice to help us with our corporately appropriate project, representing the very best of Brunel. We launched MADE IN BRUNEL in 2006, with the backing of Dame Mary Richardson, then Chief Executive of HSBC Global Education Trust. Made in Brunel was built on a strong foundation, inviting like-minded, equally talented students from across the world to form a global network. Clive was the man who just made it all work.

In 2011, Max Woźniak, student Director of Made in Brunel, wrote: 'Every year, all of you add to the heart and soul that pours into Made in Brunel. Thank you'. Clive Gee has been a key part of the project's heart and soul since we created it; working so hard to support each student team to carry the brand forwards every year. It's a bit like the Olympic torch, carried by different representatives, all sharing the same passion, but someone ensures the flame's always there to be passed on to the next generation. Clive provided the underlying continuity of the brand.

So subtle is Clive's presence in the project that most people will only glance his name as one of the book's Editors. To those lucky enough to have worked with him, Clive has been an empowering, knowledge-sharing, continuity-providing individual, passing on the brand's DNA across each generation of students. In many of the books, Clive wrote eloquently about the brand.

In 2013 (out of the blue) Directors Ben Clarke and Kat Harris invited Clive to put pen to paper.

'It is strange to think of how controversial Made in Brunel was at its inception and for many years along the way. The idea that the University would take final year student work off-campus and give a team of, already heavily overworked, finalists the responsibility of showcasing it, not just for themselves, but as a statement about the whole University, was contentious to say the least. Luckily, one common denominator of Made in Brunel teams and the University staff who work with them has been a certain level of stubbornness when faced with these sorts of challenges. My job is really to back up the Made in Brunel team and to try and provide reassurance along the way. I am also a little bit protective of the fact that Made in Brunel has to stand for excellence and quality, so my goal is usually to make sure that nothing gets in the way of the team achieving this. That plus a certain level of financial alchemy, a lot of proofreading and providing tea and biscuits to hard-pressed managers along the way'.

In 2015 (Fresh Perspectives) Director Alex Millington said "The team would like to thank Clive Gee for all his support throughout this year. Without his guidance, our ambitious ideas would not have been brought to fruition".

Clive recently left Brunel to build a new life as Development Manager, Edinburgh Napier University. We wanted to say how proud we are of his considerable input to the project. As he put it, 'it is a badge of honour that only those with similar battle scars can understand'. At the Showcases, he loved seeing past Made in Brunel teams as they met at alumni events. Clive has, over 15 years, provided much-needed consistency, allowing each new group of final year students the freedom to develop a new flexible variation of the main brand, which he wholeheartedly believed was a vital part of the University; we all loved working with him.

In 2018 (emerging) Directors Georgia Williams and Samuel Gutheridge broadened the brand to include Level 1, Level 2, Masters, PhD students and research projects. In the 2018 book, Clive was now at the top of the list thanked by the whole team.

In 2019 (futures) Directors Bethany Wale & Bradley Godbold moved the brand into a new colourful iteration. Clive was there, with Paul Josse, the duo who tirelessly empowered the students, enabling them to create

Made in Brunel. Together, Clive and Paul have been the wind beneath the students' wings, creating the support, practical help, historic knowledge, brand understanding and management of the budget.

Normally, we would have gathered together at Bargehouse in June for our final show. Clive, present students, many many alumni, staff and friends would all have been there to celebrate his time here. This celebration will have to wait, but we just wanted to say that you did a fantastic job and Made in Brunel is what it is, because of you. So, from all the Made in Brunel teams and graduates, globally, who had the privilege of working with you, we say thank you for your extraordinary dedication, passion and friendship. You are now a lifetime honorary fellow of Made in Brunel and we all look forward to seeing you again soon.

Paul Turnock
Former Director, Product Design and Product
Design Engineering and Founder of Made in Brunel

STUDENT DIRECTORY

Mia Alamo
Industrial Design and Technology BA
mia.alamo@virginmedia.com
@mia_alamo

32, 143, 168

Toby Allen
Industrial Design and Technology BA
toby5allen@gmail.com

33, 143

Charlotte Ansell
Industrial Design and Technology BA
Inception Group
charlotte.ansell@yahoo.co.uk
@Anselldesigns

Charlotte Bassett
Product Design Engineering BSc
Charles Austen Pumps
charlotte.e.bassett@gmail.com
@charlotte.bassett

34

Caitlin Beer
Industrial Design and Technology BA
Brunel University London
caitlin.beer@icloud.com

35, 139, 169

Helen Bellhouse
Industrial Design and Technology BA
helenbellhouse@icloud.com
@hub.design

36, 149

Yash Bhansali
Product Design BSc
Integrity UK, Foley Designs
bhansali.y88@gmail.com
@ybhansali.design

37, 155

Tanaka Bofu
Industrial Design and Technology BA
t_bofu@hotmail.co.uk
@tek_dsgn

141

Charlie Boyle
Product Design Engineering BSc
Wahl & Ross
charlieb983@gmail.com
@charlieboyledesign

38, 147

Tom Brew
Industrial Design and Technology BA
tbrew@hotmail.co.uk

39

Arthur Brooks
Industrial Design and Technology BA
Armour Home
abrooks@hotmail.co.uk

40, 129, 170

Jake Brown
Product Design Engineering BSc
jake.brown.design6699@gmail.com

41

Emily Browne
Product Design Engineering BSc
Christ's Hospital School
ejabrowne@gmail.com

42

Alexander Burgess
Product Design BSc
LEGO
alex.conrad.burgess@gmail.com
alexconradburgess.myportfolio.com

43

Peter Bushell
Product Design Engineering BSc
BotsAndUs
bushell.peter@gmail.com

44, 158

Samuel Bušovský
Industrial Design and Technology BA
Adamastor
s.busovsky@outlook.com
@busovskydesign

45, 149

Imogen Campbell-Heanue
Product Design Engineering BSc
Brunel University
immie.cch@googlemail.com
@_imogencampbell

46, 171

Arun Chalotra
Industrial Design and Technology BA
Inside Out Contracts Ltd.
arunchalotra@aol.co.uk
arunchalotra.com

47, 151

Yili Chen
Product Design BSc
yilichen295@gmail.com
@yililili_chen

48

Shujie Chen
Industrial Design and Technology BA
841673135@qq.com

49

Niamh Cogley-Rock
Industrial Design and Technology BA
Dyson
niamhrockdesign@gmail.com
@niamhrockdesign

50, 155, 172

Hannah Coombs
Industrial Design and Technology BA
Mondelez International
hannahrcoombs@outlook.com
hannahcoombsdesign.com
@hannahcoombsx

51, 173, 139

Pippa Copeland
Product Design BSc
Shark Ninja
pippacopeland@outlook.com

52, 159

Harry Cozens
Industrial Design and Technology BA
Integrity UK Ltd
harrycozens@live.com

53, 143

Shivy Das
Industrial Design and Technology BA
Biohm
shivydas1@gmail.com

54, 131

Angharad Davies
Product Design BSc
Guy's and St. Thomas' NHS
angharad.davies1@gmail.com
@anniethegoodlife

55

Jack Day
Industrial Design and Technology BA
Brunel University
jackdaydesigns@gmail.com
@jack_e_day

56, 139

Coleman Deady Ridge
Industrial Design and Technology BA
Philips Lighting
colemandeadyridge@gmail.com

57

Chris Delaney
Industrial Design and Technology BA
chrisdelan18@gmail.com
@itsdeldesign

58, 137

Miles Egbuchiem
Industrial Design and Technology BA
Ogilvy
miles.egbuchiem@gmail.com
@miles.egb

59

George Farren
Product Design Engineering BSc
Plexus
georgeafarren@gmail.com

60, 160

Justine Fernandez
Product Design Engineering BSc
Sixth Sense Events
raven07@hotmail.co.uk
@raven29034

61, 135

Elise Filleul
Industrial Design and Technology BA
UCB Pharmaceuticals
elise.rebecca.filleul@gmail.com

62, 151, 174

Robert Foulds
Industrial Design and Technology BA
Batch.works
rwfoulds@gmail.com
rwfoulds.myportfolio.com
@rwfoulds

63

Angus Galton
Industrial Design and Technology BA
angusgalton@gmail.com
galtonprjx.com
@gltnprjx

64, 153

Andrew Gardner
Industrial Design and Technology BA
Futurama ltd
andrew.s.gardner@sky.com

65, 153

Matt Gardner
Product Design Engineering BSc
iSi-Sanitaire.fr
matthewgardner1997@gmail.com
@mattgardner.des

66, 131

Georgina Hatch
Product Design Engineering BSc
Politecnico di Milano
georgina-h@live.co.uk

72

Sirtaj Singh Ghata-Aura
Industrial Design and Technology BA
Nissan Technical Centre Europe
staj.aura@sauradesign.com
sauradesign.com
@sauradesign

67, 133

Fatima Hermosin Acasuso
Product Design Engineering BSc
Williams Advanced Engineering
fatimaher1998@gmail.com

73, 155

Charlie Gilks
Product Design Engineering BSc
Silver
charliegilksdesign@gmail.com
@charliegilks

68, 147

Jesslin Ho
Product Design Engineering BSc
John Cullen Lighting, NIO
jesslinho@gmail.com

74

Sam Harding
Product Design Engineering BSc
Ember Cycles
hardingdesign@gmail.com
embercycles.com
@samhardingstagram

69

Joseph Irvine
Product Design Engineering BSc
joseph@irvineassociates.co.uk
josephirvinedesign.co.uk

75

Evelyn Grace Harris
Product Design BSc
Marlow Integrated Design Ltd
evieharris@hotmail.com
@evelyn_grace_design

70, 161

Jonathan James
Product Design Engineering BSc
Shark Ninja
jonfjames@googlemail.com
@jjproductdesign

76, 162

Amin Haruna
Industrial Design and Technology BA
San Francisco State University
haruna.amin@gmail.com
aminharuna.com
@amin.haruna

71, 133

Jan Nicholas Janiurek
Industrial Design and Technology BA
Ember Cycles
nickjaniurek@aol.com
embercycles.com
@embercycles

77

We Are Made in Brunel | Directory

Viraj Javaharlal
Product Design BSc
LEGO Systems A/S
vee_java@icloud.com

78, 155

Skyler Riz Manalili
Product Design BSc
skyler.Manalili@outlook.com

84

Elias Kara
Industrial Design and Technology BA
karaeliasm@gmail.com
@eliasmkara

79

Oliver Martin
Industrial Design and Technology BA
Numatic International
olliemarkmartin@gmail.com
designingom.com
@designing_om

85, 129

Megan King
Industrial Design and Technology BA
CCD Design & Ergonomics
megan.jane.king@outlook.com

80, 137, 175

Preetpaul Matharoo
Product Design Engineering BSc
Ideaworks
preetmatharoowork@gmail.com

86

Thomas Knipe
Industrial Design and Technology BA
Vanberlo
thomas.knipe@gmail.com
@angry_jacked_renders

81, 133

Jacob McAdam
Product Design Engineering BSc
Alvan Blanch Dev Co
jacob.mcadam@googlemail.com

87

Tanaka Kungwengwe
Industrial Design and Technology BA
Cambridge Consultants
kungwengwe@outlook.com

82, 151

Stuart Meredith
Product Design Engineering BSc
stuart.meredith@outlook.com
@stuart.meredith

88, 147

Oliver Lambert
Industrial Design and Technology BA
Radiant Architectural Lighting
ollie.j.lambert@gmail.com
@ollie__lambert

83, 151

Toby Middleton
Industrial Design and Technology BA
Lozi Designs
tobystanleymidd@gmail.com
tsmiddleton.com

89, 143

Edmund Miles
Industrial Design and Technology BA
West London Shooting School
edmund@eohm.co.uk
@eohm_design

143

Oliver Minns
Industrial Design and Technology BA
Castleton Signs
olliejminns@hotmail.co.uk
@ollieminns

90

Max Mitchell
Industrial Design and Technology BA
Haberdashery
max@mmitchell.design
@mmitchell.design

91, 143

Roxana Mobasheri
Industrial Design and Technology BA
roxana.mobasheri@gmail.com

92

Anavi Modi
Product Design BSc
anvimodi176@gmail.com
@anvimodi_

93

Caitlyn Morton
Industrial Design and Technology BA
caitlyn.morton54@gmail.com

149

Lewis Muggeridge
Industrial Design and Technology BA
lewismuggeridge@gmail.com
lewismuggeridge.com
@muggeridgedesign

94, 147

Nivedhaa Muthu
Product Design BSc
IBM UK
nivedhaa.muthu@gmail.com

95, 155, 176

Jake O'Sullivan
Industrial Design and Technology BA
Jaguar Land Rover
jake.osullivan96@hotmail.com
@jakeosullivan_design

96

Ruby Ovenden
Industrial Design and Technology BA
Hollaway Studio Architects
rubyovenden@gmail.com
rubyovenden.wixsite.com/portfolio
@ruby_o_design

97, 139

David Paling
Product Design BSc
dpa Lighting Consultants
djpaling65@gmail.com
@d.pdesign

98, 163

Arphatsara Paowana
Industrial Design and Technology BA
LEGO System A/S
arphatsarap@hotmail.com
@arphatsarap

99, 131

Seb Parker
Industrial Design and Technology BA
Avon Protection
ssrparker@gmail.com

100, 133, 164

Katie Price
Industrial Design and Technology BA
Nulty Bespoke
katieaprice.design@gmail.com
katieprice-design.com
@katiepricedesign_

105, 129, 179

Vasily Parshin
Product Design Engineering BSc
vasparshin@gmail.com
@vas__design

165

Owen Purvis
Product Design BSc
LEGO Group, Visual Energy
opurvisdesign@gmail.com

106

Andrew Pickering
Industrial Design and Technology BA
Bosch
a.pickering.design@gmail.com
@ap.industrial.design

101, 131

Isaac Reeves
Product Design BSc
Haberdashery
hello@isaacreeves.com
isaacreeves.com
@isaaceor

107, 180

Maria Alejandra Pinilla Pease
Industrial Design and Technology BA
IBM
mpinilla1996@gmail.com
mariapinilla.myportfolio.com

102, 155, 177

Natalia Rehakova
Industrial Design and Technology BA
Identity Consulting
nataliacrehakova@gmail.com

108, 135, 181

Jamie Pinkham
Product Design Engineering BSc
MERU - QinetiQ
jamiepinkham@hotmail.com
@pinkhamdesign

103

Conor Richey
Industrial Design and Technology BA
Beco Pets
contact@conorricheydesign.com
@conorricheydesign

109, 131, 182

Victoria Poizer
Industrial Design and Technology BA
Batch.works
victoriapoizer@ntlworld.com

104, 137, 178

Isidora Rivera Vollmer
Industrial Design and Technology BA
isidorarivera@gmail.com
behance.net/isidorariveravollmer
@irv_designs

110, 145

Dante Roberts
Product Design BSc
danteroberts.972@gmail.com

111, 183

Lauren Jane Rushen
Industrial Design and Technology BA
FutureNova
lauren_rushen@live.co.uk
@laurenjanedesign_

112, 149

Omar Rushton
Industrial Design and Technology BA
Michael Young Studio
orushton@gmail.com
@omarrushton

113, 135

Amber Sayers
Industrial Design and Technology BA
therefore product design consultants
ambersayersdesign@gmail.com
ambersayers.com
@amgsayers

114, 129, 184

Max Schöpp
Industrial Design and Technology BA
RNS Meals
schopp.design@gmail.com

115, 149

Kevin Shaji
Industrial Design and Technology BA
San Francisco State University
kevin.alias.shaji@gmail.com
Kevinshaji.com
@Kevin_Alias_Shaji

116, 133

Ruoyu Shi
Product Design BSc
shiruoyu465@163.com

117

Luke Smith
Product Design BSc
TU Delft (The Netherlands)
lukemasmith.design@gmail.com
lukemasmithdesign.myportfolio.com
@lukemasmith.design

118, 129

Harry Snow
Product Design Engineering BSc
Modus Furniture
harrysnow9@googlemail.com

119, 147

Luke Tolchard
Industrial Design and Technology BA
Avery WePrint
luketolchard@gmail.com
luketolchard.com
@luketolchard

120, 139

Stephanie Tomlinson
Industrial Design and Technology BA
Queen Elizabeth's School
stephanie_tomlinson1@outlook.com
@by_stomlinson

153

Max Trafford
Product Design BSc
Formula One
maxtraffordphotography@gmail.com
maxtrafford.co.uk
@max.trafford

185

Naomi Tucker
Product Design BSc
The Imagination Factory
itsnaomitucker@gmail.com
@itsnaomitucker

121, 141

Daniel Valentine
Industrial Design and Technology BA
David Lewis Designers, Disney and
Cambridge Consultants
dantval@aol.com
dtvdesign.com
@dtvdesign   **122, 151**

William Vickery
Industrial Design and Technology BA
CRL, Studio Make Believe
will.j.vickery@gmail.com
willvickery.com/
@will.vickery

151

Charlie Wilson
Industrial Design and Technology BA
charlieseanw@gmail.com
@charliew.98

123, 141

Ben Younger
Industrial Design and Technology BA
PiXL Club Limited
younger.ben@sky.com
@_boydesign

124, 153

Minnan Yu
Product Design Engineering BSc
Loowatt Ltd.
yminnan@yahoo.com
@rryu706

125

POSTGRADUATE

Made in Brunel 2019/20

Directors
Jack Day
Amber Sayers

Publications Managers
Charlie Boyle
Isaac Reeves

Web Managers
Hannah Coombs
Maria Alejandra Pinilla Pease

Social Media Managers
Conor Richey
Max Trafford

New Designers Manager
Angharad Davies

Events Managers
Caitlin Beer
Oliver Martin

Branding Managers
Charlie Gilks
Ruby Ovenden

Marketing Managers
Pippa Copeland
Katie Price

Planning Managers
Toby Middleton
Luke Smith

Masters Liaison
David Paling
Alejandro Romero Rosell
Kyle May
Hsin Lun Wu
Tosin Folarin
Ashiq Nazir Rafia

Research Liaison
Naomi Tucker

Communications Manager
Charlotte Willis

Design Workshop Liaison
Emily Lucas

Thank you

At the beginning of this academic year and this Made in Brunel, we could not have imagined the circumstances in which it would end. Although our traditional showcase event was not possible, we have still managed to share our work and ideas in brand news ways, and under the most challenging of conditions. As such, and not to mention our events earlier in the year, the success of this year's Made in Brunel has called for an exceptional effort from many people, staff, student and beyond - we owe all of you a huge debt of gratitude.

Paul...

If you ask any Brunel Design student what they do during a work-related crisis, you can almost guarantee they'll say their first port of call is to wander down to Tower B to find the one and only Paul Josse. Which is why, once again, we are saying a huge thank you.

For helping us bring our hare-brained schemes to fruition, and for building us fantastic displays such as the ones on show during the Pop-Up in Shoreditch. All whilst keeping us sane in the process.

This year has been tough from start to finish. The start saw the departure of the wonderful Clive Gee, which resulted Paul experiencing some previously unseen demand for his services, which of course he dealt with as pragmatically as ever. COVID-19 also through a spanner into the works, which Paul took in his stride, spending many weeks fighting our corner and ensuring that despite all the confusion and despair, MIB would still produce something of worth.

Made in Brunel would not be possible without all your hard work Paul. From the whole MIB team, Thank You!

The Book

Editors

Isaac Reeves
Charlie Boyle

Photography

Patrick Quayle
Max Trafford
Conor Richey
Paul Josse
Bella Li
Isaac Reeves

Special Thanks

Paul Josse
Marjan Angoshtari
Dr Danah Abdulla
Dr Vanja Garaj
Ryan Smith
Steve McGonigal
Dr Busayawan Lam
Dr Eujin Pei
Dr Fabrizio Ceschin
Paul Turnock
and, most importantly
The Made in Brunel class of 2020

WE ARE
MADE IN BRUNEL

ISBN: 9781908549464

Printed by Geoff Neal Group

www.madeinbrunel.com

Made in Brunel
Brunel University London
Uxbridge
UB8 3PH

Editors: Isaac Reeves and Charlie Boyle

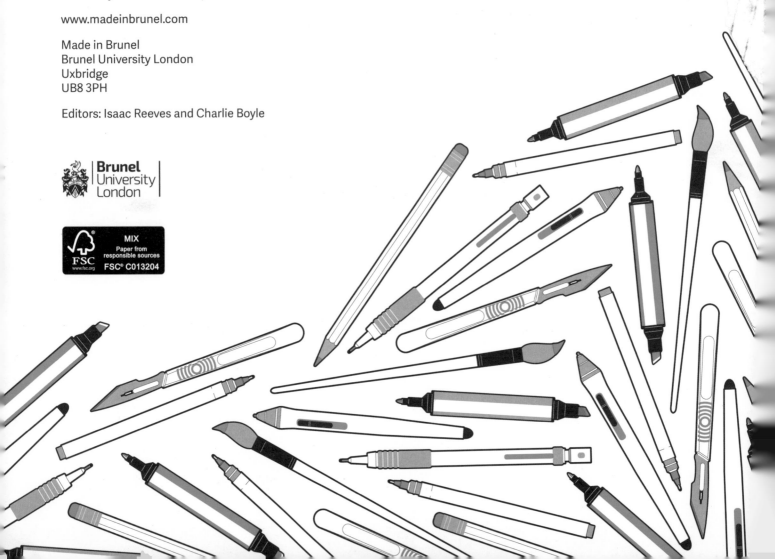